DR. BRESKY'S 9PT SYSTEM

GUIDE TO

CARING FOR YOURSELF

AN INSPIRATIONAL, SCIENTIFIC ROAD MAP TO CARE FOR YOURSELF (AND OTHERS.)

Wrtten & Compiled by
Arnold Bresky, M.D.
With Amy Wall

PUBLISHING

Dedication

I dedicate this book to my wonderful and loving daughter Lisa Bresky Howe and her wonderful husband Tony Howe. I also dedicate this book to my special and loyal son Gary Scott Bresky and his lovely wife Lauren.

I dedicate this book to all my formal and informal supportive teachers.

I dedicate this book to my precious granddaughters, Rachel Howe and Gillian Howe.

Finally, I dedicate this book to the growing millions of holy and decent caregivers in the world.

Published by: A&B W Publishing
(310) 282-9937

ISBN 978-1-60643-511-3
First Edition

Acknowledgements

I first want to acknowledge my lovely daughter Lisa Bresky Howe and my wonderful son Gary Scott Bresky for their enduring love, patience, and loyalty.

Bill and Amy Wilson should be acknowledged for their perseverance in every phase of this long process. I also need to acknowledge Charlotte for her additions to the book.

My long list of patients should be acknowledged because they taught me so very much. I must especially acknowledge my loving mother and father who instilled in me the love of learning, knowledge and clear worthwhile values. I stand on the shoulders of all my teachers and especially the Greek philosophers, 2,500 years ago, who promulgated the principle of Holistic Medicine. One cannot forget Maimonides, the Father of Modern Medicine, who said, 1,000 years ago, that the best medicine is preventive medicine. All the world's basic scientific researchers must be acknowledged because I am an applied scientist who uses their findings in a user-friendly manner to reduce suffering.

Lastly, as a healer, I want to acknowledge the Almighty for helping me to understand that I must repair the imperfect world and reach out to people in need. We judge a society by how they deal with their very young and very old. I want to thank the Almighty for giving me an evergreen code of ethical behavior. In the final analysis, we all must acknowledge that when we alleviate another's suffering, we are alleviating our own suffering.

Table of Contents

Preface and About Dr. Bresky

I helped write this book to introduce the world to the Brain Tune Up® Doctor and his system, and provide them with this inspirational, scientific road map.

In 1999, my grandmother died after a difficult battle with dementia. The management of her decline and death was excruciatingly painful for my family and me. Then in 2007, my husband's grandmother also passed away from complications of dementia. I was shocked at how little had changed in the fight his family went through compared to mine over eight years earlier.

In what felt like a case of divine intervention, we happened to meet Dr. Bresky the day after the funeral of my husband's grandmother. Bill shared his family experience with Dr. Bresky, who has heard my husband's story thousands of times before while treating dementia sufferers and their caregivers.

Dr. Bresky invited us to see his patients in action and witness the results of their therapy. We were amazed at the beautiful artwork, engrossing music activities, and thousands of brain games invented by Dr. Bresky, as well as the countless stories of people whose lives had been changed by the person they affectionately call the Brain Tune Up® Doctor. We knew immediately that a program like the Brain Tune Up® 9 Pt. System was what our families needed during our bouts with dementia.

Let me give you a brief glimpse into the background of this amazing doctor who Bill and I are so privileged to know. Dr. Bresky is a son of the depression era who definitely has a motivating "type A" personality. The doctor's story plays like many success stories. He overachieved his way from the streets of Brooklyn to eventually surpass the American dream in his success as a surgeon.

During the 1960's, medical degrees dedicated to healing an aging population were rarely offered by medical schools. Albert Einstein College of Medicine was no different. So Dr. Bresky chose the medical field where he knew he'd get to smile and laugh every time he went to work. You guessed it....he became an OB-GYN delivering babies. After building a highly successful medical career delivering thousands of babies, performing thousands of surgeries and opening highly successful child-birth clinics, Dr. Bresky left his success as an OB-GYN behind to embark on a spiritual journey to heal the seniors of the world. In typical fashion, he decided to teach himself how to be of medical service to seniors and heal the world from the "top down" instead of the "bottom up".

His first endeavor was to open an athletic gym dedicated solely to seniors in 1992. He immediately noticed the positive effects of physical activity on his patrons' memories. This so intrigued him that he threw himself into studying every book available on memory and the brain. By 1995, Dr. Bresky was actively creating problem-solving games and creating sketch art for his patients to draw to stimulate their brains. Once again he saw wonderful results. In 1996, Albert Einstein College of Medicine officially changed his medical designation to **Preventive Gerontologist**. Meanwhile, his Alzheimer's patients and caregivers kept smiling and growing new brain cells, while participating in Dr. Bresky's "seasoned" bingo and horse racing games.

By 1998, he was developing special word games, adding music therapy, and customizing thousands of brain exercise activities based on the needs of the patient. He then started introducing techniques that evolved from his rabbi training, national wellness movement participation, and four years of medical school psychiatric studies. These techniques united all the components of his program into a true "mind, body and soul" approach to brain health. By 1999, Dr. Bresky was telling every medical professional who would listen that his patients' memory scores were holding strong, or improving, using his therapeutic recreations. At the time, the medical community wasn't ready to embrace him or his unorthodox program.

However, research has finally caught up with Dr. Bresky's pioneering programs. Recent clinical studies by top medical schools and neurological researchers are proving what the Brain Tune Up® Doctor has been espousing for years, that cognitive behavioral therapy slows cognitive decline and improves quality of life. Dr. Bresky's system has been quietly helping patients for 15 years with a base of thousands of thankful caregivers and patients, and he continues to see patients in his practice today.

Amy Wall
Book Editor and Family Caregiver

Introduction

What is the number one secret to caregiver success?

If you are like most caregivers, your answer probably has something to do with giving quality care to your loved one. Good communication with the physician, you might answer, or constant, consistent visits and phone calls. Maybe you would choose keeping a careful eye on medication, or ensuring good nutrition, or maintaining medical equipment. The list could go on and on.

Odds are good, however, that your answer was focused on the loved one you are caring for. And if so, your answer was wrong. Why? Because the number one secret to caregiver success is to take care of the caregiver first. In fact, everyone is a caregiver. You are a caregiver for yourself.

This book refers to caregivers throughout. Don't be confused, it will show you how to take care of yourself and if you are providing care for a loved one it will show you how to take them along on the journey as well.

Oprah Winfrey, in *Making Connections* says, "It's the support and care and love that you give yourself that gives you the real strength to care for others." She's right. Oprah knows the secret of taking care of others is to take care of yourself.

The simple truth is that it is not possible to provide good care for a loved one without caring for yourself first. My Brain Tune Up 9 Pt. System offers nine important and easy ways in which you can learn to care for yourself first.

But, you are a caregiver and life is one long scramble. Whether you are a full-time or part-time caregiver, there is rarely a spare minute for anything. You don't have time to care for yourself because you're so busy caring for others. You rise with the dawn in order to have time to check in on your mother before you go to work, and after work you rush back to take her to a doctor's appointment. After the doctor's appointment you have to go pick your son up from football practice or your daughter from the soccer field, and then go by the grocery store and home to cook dinner. And when you get home, there's a call from the doctor and you need to go get a prescription filled. Does this sound familiar?

This story, or a variation of it, is the reality of day to day life for millions of caregivers. So when you hear me say that you need to take care of yourself first, you put it off. Who has time for self-care? Who has time to enjoy life? You do. You must find time for it, and following my 9 Pt. System will make it easy.

Not taking time to care for yourself is a sure path to anger, depression and ill health. And then you're not good for anybody. You can't possibly maintain the reserves of energy that you need to be of service as a caregiver if you are constantly stressed and tired.

You're not the only one facing this problem. Statistics reveal that over 44 million people in this country suffer from issues related to caregiving.[1] This is one important reason why I developed the 9 Pt. System.

I've developed and successfully applied every single one of these Points based on what I've seen in my medical practice working with seniors and their caregivers for over a decade, plus extensive scientific research. I've also made certain that each activity is easy to add to your already over-committed life.

You may think I don't understand the challenges of being a caregiver. You might wonder how I could possibly understand how the course of your day plays out. Believe me, I do.

I started out using many of the therapeutic techniques in this book back in the early 1980s, when I ran an alternative childbirth center. I loved bringing babies into the world in a soothing, natural manner. However, I got even more excited when I discovered that the holistic, integrative techniques I was using at the beginning of life were also applicable to improving the quality of life for people at the end of their lives.

I was one of the promoters of the original hospice concept, and my hospital at the time was the second in the nation to utilize hospice care. Since 1997, I have devoted my time, money and energy to geriatric care as a Preventive Gerontologist. What, you might ask, is a Preventive Gerontologist? A Preventive Gerontologist teaches people of any age how to age both gracefully and successfully. It is my mission to repair the world from the top down. This is my passion, and I live it every day.

We live in a miraculous age. Marvelous developments make good brain health something we can control as the years advance. It doesn't matter how old a person is, or even how far their cognitive decline has advanced. With the Brain Tune Up 9 Pt. System, there's always room for hope and improvement. I have studies that prove it. Over and over again we've seen immediate results from patients embarking on my Brain Tune Up 9 Pt. System. And now, you as the caregiver have access to this life-changing information, too.

Let me tell you a story that illustrates how my 9 Pt. System can have a dramatic effect on the lives of the patient with dementia *and* the caregiver. One of my patients, W.E., was a 76-year-old man who had been clinically diagnosed with Alzheimer's. W.E.'s wife was his primary caregiver and she noticed his memory loss. Not only that, but W.E. also exhibited paranoia, agitation, and irritability. He forgot names of relatives, failed to recognize his relatives, misplaced his keys, and couldn't remember if he had eaten a meal recently.

W.E.'s wife had no experience with caregiving and her husband's memory lapses and care requirements terrified her. She was willing to do anything to salvage the situation. W.E. began my Brain Tune Up System. At first, because he was suffering from chronic stress, low self-esteem, and depression the going was tough. But one of the goals I got from him was that his lifelong dream had been to visit England with his wife.

Anyone seeing W.E. in the condition he was in when I began working with him would think this was unlikely. However, we persevered. The results were nothing short of astounding. Over two years, W.E. experienced measurable improvement in his cognitive functioning. His short-term memory improved, he could pay attention with both eyes and ears for nine seconds, and he had less difficulty with judgment and problem solving. Life improved for his wife, too—she had fewer symptoms of caregiver burnout. There was less chaos in her life and she had a much better sense of control. But the best thing was that W.E. improved so much that he and his wife were able to take that long-awaited trip to England. I have the T-shirt they brought me from Stonehenge as proof!

It is because of results like this that I have written this book, so that I can share this vital information with everyone who needs it. This means not only those providing care for Alzheimer's and dementia sufferers, but those dealing with other conditions and diseases that can cause memory loss such as brain trauma or injury, stroke, Parkinson's disease, Multiple Sclerosis, open heart surgery, sleep apnea, adult attention deficit disorder, chemo and radiation therapy, mild cognitive impairment, congestive heart failure and chronic obstructive pulmonary disease.

Throughout this book you'll find tips and techniques to integrate the recommendations into the daily flow of your life. Taking time for yourself will give you more energy and vitality. With that increased energy and vitality you'll be able to accomplish more in less time during the course of your day. Remember, taking just one small step a day can add up to big results.

You've taken on a lot. You're entitled to feel sorry for yourself sometimes. But be vigilant. Keep it to a minimum. Chronic worry, fear and negativity keep you up at night and drain the joy from your day. Action stops and you become paralyzed. Instead, consider putting the time you might waste on negativity into participating in the 9 Pt. System.

Before we get started, let's take a quick look at my Brain Tune Up® 9 Pt. System, so you know what to expect. Here they are:

1. Fun and Laughter
2. Relaxation, Meditation and Prayer
3. Tunes Rx
4. Sleep
5. Physical Exercise
6. Brain Tune Up® Eating Plan
7. Hydration
8. Brain Exercises and Art Rx
9. Kindness

Take it slow and easy and don't try to do everything at once. You might want to set aside a half-hour or so to implement some of the ideas at first. Once you see how much better they make you feel, you will be willing to take even more time. And remember, all of the Points can and should be done with the loved one you are caring for.

Once you're familiar with all 9 Points of my system, you'll find incorporating them into your daily life, as well as the time you spend with your loved one, *is* easy *and* fun! The Brain Tune Up 9 Pt. System will help you make the most of every day, live a healthy, well-balanced, enjoyable existence and increase the quality of life for you and your loved one.

Ready? Then let's get started.

Point 1: Fun and Laughter

Fun and laughter are *necessities* in everyone's life and one of the most important Points of my Brain Tune Up 9 Pt. System. You may wonder why I chose to address this Point of my program first when other Points may seem more innovative or essential. That's easy.

Fun and enjoyment are the first things a caregiver gives up. You have responsibilities—serious things that need your attention. When life gets too serious, life becomes a bore. When life becomes a bore, life becomes a chore. When life becomes a chore, who really wants to live it?

Caregivers most often forego their own needs and even basic requirements to fulfill the needs of their loved one. Caregiving is not a single task that is taken care of quickly. No, being a caregiver is a long-term commitment and sometimes long-term can mean way longer than you might expect. One of the problems with caregiving is that often there seems to be no end in sight, just a lengthy period of stressful caretaking activities.[2] All of this commonly culminates in caregiver burnout. Depression among caregivers is more prevalent than among others their age and as many as 40% of caregivers for sufferers of dementia, experience depression.[3] Furthermore, studies have shown that depression may actually put you more at risk for developing dementia yourself.[4]

Is this *really* what *you* signed up for? Some days you may wish that there was someone else who could take over for you, though you know full well that's not going to happen. There is good news, however, and that is the simple fact that depression and fun can't co-exist. If you have to live with one or the other, the choice seems pretty obvious. Which will you choose? Most of us will choose to have fun.

Do it before you reach a crisis. Make it a daily ritual, even if it's only for a few minutes. It's my hope that this program will show you how to turn those first few minutes into your entire life. How to make *everything* you do fun.

As we progress, I'll show you ways to combine the Points of the Brain Tune Up 9 Pt. System. Ways to have fun and build your brain bank, or cognitive reserve, at the same time. Ways to have fun and get physical exercise at the same time. When you see how easy it is to combine many of these Points, you'll see how easy it is to live this program.

There are so many ways to incorporate fun, laughter and social interaction into your day. Just putting your brain to the task of figuring it out will be fun. Probably a lot more fun than the thoughts you currently dwell on, especially if you're dealing with caregiver burnout and/or depression.

DEPRESSION

Are you having a hard time imagining *anything* as fun? You're burnt out. Being burnt out can lead to depression and depression kills brain cells. Please make an appointment with a physician if you've experienced any of the following for longer than two weeks:

- Tiredness of either the physical or mental kind
- Sadness
- Anxiety
- Decreased sex drive
- Sexual dysfunction
- Emptiness
- Lack of pleasure in your usual activities
- Weight loss
- Weight gain
- Stomach upsets
- Digestive problems
- Memory difficulties
- Finding it hard to concentrate
- Feeling stressed out
- Physical aches and pains that linger
- Feeling helpless
- Feeling worthless
- Feeling unexcited about the future
- Unexplained, recurring fits of crying[5]

If any of the above apply to you *stop what you're doing right now*. Think about what you could do that would bring you *joy*. It doesn't matter what anybody else thinks, what matters is you.

Remember, caring for others starts with caring for yourself.

Think of something that would bring *you* joy. Make it your top priority. Sounds strange, doesn't it? But you'll get the hang of it. And once you get the hang of it, you'll enjoy it so much you won't want to stop.

Do you enjoy reading novels? When was the last time you picked one up? Buy one and read for a half hour before bed. When was the last time you had sex? Tell your spouse Dr. Bresky ordered it! (I'm looking forward to the thank you cards!) Do you love to dance? Put on some music and dance around the living room.

Maybe you like to sing. Belt out a song. Do it in the car on the way to work, or while you're in the shower. Better yet, go to karaoke. Or maybe it's time to take the dog to the park and throw a Frisbee. Go shopping, or see a movie. Do whatever makes you happy and relaxed.

And no feeling guilty about taking this time for yourself, either. How can you have fun when you're feeling guilty? And remember, fun and depression can't co-exist. Also recall that depression is common among caregivers. So, my rule is not only an ounce of prevention is worth a ton of cure, but also that an ounce of fun is worth a ton of anti-depressants.

LAUGHTER

While you are planning activities that make you happy, put anything that makes you laugh at the top of the list. Laughter releases positive chemicals in your brain and is good for the immune system.[6] How many depressed people do you see laughing?

Your loved one needs to have fun too. They need to laugh and spend quality time with others. Laughter is very healing and good for the brain. A good goal to aim for is to have nine hearty laughs a day. Yes, nine. It is not that difficult once you get going because laughter is contagious. You'll be surprised how good this simple prescription will make you feel.

Have you ever stopped to think about what laughter *is*? It is the human body (and brain's) physical reaction to something funny. Laughter causes many changes in your body as it occurs, including the contraction of up to 15 facial muscles, changes in your respiratory system and tear ducts, and changes in many of your body's muscle groups.

As it causes these changes, laughter is reaping great health benefits on your body. It helps to balance the immune system, which helps to keep you healthy and free of disease. Laughter decreases levels of stress hormones (we'll learn more about the dangers of stress in Point 2.) It can also clear the respiratory tract. Best of all, laughter can be as useful to your body as an entire exercise workout. Laughing 100 times equals the work out you would get from pedaling for 15 minutes on a stationary bicycle. Now that is a great reason to find things to laugh about!

Laughter is great for your psychological health also. In its simplest form, laughter is a release. Instead of holding in all your emotions, laughter gives you a way to set them free. If you've ever had the experience of helplessly laughing for an extended period of time, you've discovered how cathartic it can be.

But besides its beneficial effects on the body, laughter has many social benefits also. Researchers believe that laughter began as a relief among tribes after a dangerous situation. This points to laughter's ability to create bonds among people. Laughter in groups tends to occur when there is trust and comfort amongst its members.[7]

Researchers have also found that people with an optimistic outlook on life actually live longer than those who harbor pessimistic views. Optimists typically live 19% longer lives![8]

BEHAVIOR CHALLENGES

Perhaps your loved one feels abandoned by those they love. Moving into a care facility or other issues our elderly loved ones face can trigger the fear of abandonment, which is an overwhelming fear that is basic to human psychology. It causes people to behave in unusual and desperate ways. Fear of abandonment can trigger the same physical and chemical reaction in your body as an addict going through withdrawals. The difference is that your loved one is craving people instead of a drug or alcohol.[9] Your loved one may be feeling useless, unnoticed, insignificant and nonexistent. These feelings can often cause people to lash out negatively to get any attention they can.

Be tolerant, sympathetic and kind during these episodes. I know it may be difficult to react this way to such aggression, but understand what is going on and recognize the problem. It will be far easier for you to be tolerant, sympathetic and kind if you are following the 9 Points, and taking good care of yourself. It will also help to remember the proverb, he who seeks good finds goodwill.

If your loved one is further along in the stages of cognitive decline, they may be cranky. And this might well make you cranky, too, because negativity has a tendency to do that. How to deal with this problem? Take a cue from my section on laughter, and laugh gently at their crankiness.

It will also help to be understanding and compassionate. Maybe you have felt that being positive is impossible, given the stresses of your situation. But following the suggestions in this book will ease your mind and show you a positive way to respond to the caregiving relationship. Understanding and compassion will naturally follow.

People in the moderate and advanced stages of cognitive decline can be challenging to communicate with. It may seem impossible to share enjoyable interactions. That's when it is time to get inventive.

Challenges build your brain bank, which also happens to be fortunate for you. Look at this challenge as something you can overcome. Seeing it this way relaxes you and frees your mind.

18

A stressed mind has a harder time finding solutions. Stress produces cortisol, which blocks glucose from entering brain cells.[10] A relaxed mind, with easy access to its glucose supply, comes up with creative solutions to challenges that arise. Without challenges in life how would you grow and learn and become a better person?

One of the challenges in caregiving is the role reversal that occurs when a child is now caring for a parent. It will take awhile for both people to adapt. Be kind with them while they get used to the role reversal. Be kind with yourself as you get used to your new role. Taking time to explore the 9 Points and use them faithfully will make adapting to these new roles much easier.

In the case of severe cognitive decline, your loved one may behave like a child. Treat them with the patience you'd show a child, because they're not in their right mind. Love and bless them and remember that they know not what they do. One of the most beautiful gifts you can give yourself is to stop taking the bad behavior of others personally. It's not about you. Rise above it. Forgive them. Above all else remember you are an "angel of action" in this world, be divine.

COMMUNICATION

Communicating with your loved ones can be challenging-whether they're suffering from cognitive decline or not.

In this section you'll find pointers for successful communication with *all* your loved ones, including the person you're caring for, other family members, and friends.

Communication occurs on several levels. An important thing to remember is that communication is not simply verbal. Rather, it happens in several different ways. While the spoken word is the most obvious form of communication, it's also important to consider the energy and action behind the words, and the person who is saying the words. For instance, you can tell someone you love them but your demeanor, expressions, and body language may tell them otherwise.[11]

Be cognizant not only of what you are saying, but how you are saying it. Use a gentle tone of voice and a relaxed posture when communicating with your loved one.

Remain serene. Maintaining a peaceful, calm energy will aid communication. Raising your voice, showing irritation, or talking too fast can raise tension.[12]

Stay in the now. Enjoy the present moment with your loved one as much as possible and don't give into bitterness or resentments about past behaviors. Let it go, stay only focused on the here and now.

Avoid arguing. You and your loved may disagree, but be certain to acknowledge that you've heard their point of view. Ultimately, it is their life and care that is at stake. At the very least, everyone wants to feel heard. [13]

Listen intently. This may be challenging, particularly if your loved one is not making much sense as you listen. But listening well is an important part of intimacy also. Everyone deserves to be heard, even those with advanced cognitive decline.

Maintain a sense of humor. As we've seen, laughter can be hugely cathartic. Having a sense of humor about your situation can help you in your communications.

Be positive. Your loved one may have a hard time understanding you, and this can get frustrating for all concerned. However, if you maintain a positive attitude, it will help your communication.

You may find yourself in a situation where your loved one dwells on unpleasant topics. Rather than attempting to get them to stop, or arguing with them, try diverting the conversation to a more pleasant topic. Distraction can work wonders![14]

I'll give you brain exercises, as well as art therapies and other Points from the Brain Tune Up 9 Pt. System that will help your loved one regain some of their mental faculties. These work, no matter what stage of cognitive decline your loved one is in. (See my Jewish Home Study in Point 8.)

Using these tools will make the time you spend with your loved one more enjoyable for you both. Wherever they are now, accept them. Forgive them when they behave badly. They know not what they do.

Frequently, our loved ones in the beginning stages of cognitive decline aren't diagnosed until there's been some progression. Early changes in communication, personality, and behavior are often misunderstood and misinterpreted.

Now that you know how important it is, make sure to have fun, laugh and engage in enjoyable social activity daily. Make sure your loved one does too. Do it together or separately.

PET THERAPY

Another way of engaging your loved one in social activity is to give them the responsibility and challenge of caring for another living being. Many studies prove that giving seniors something to care for provides many beneficial quality of life effects.

Some of these studies have shown that seniors with pets have lower blood pressure and stress, and overall go to the doctor 21% less. One study actually showed that pet owners who had experienced a heart attack had a better chance of survival in the following year. Did you know that even after simply petting a dog, both you and the dog release a multitude of beneficial hormones?[15]

Other benefits that can be experienced through pet therapy include:

- Better communication between patient and caregivers

- More and better social interaction

- A boost in self-esteem

- Higher levels of motivation

- Improvements in memory

- Encourages physical movement in brain-impaired patients

- Lessens anxiety[16]

- Helps to reduce agitation in Alzheimer's patients[17]

Isn't it amazing that interacting with a pet can have so many beneficial results? As you can see, caring for another living thing is a wonderful way to give importance and add value to you and your loved one's life.

PUT IT INTO ACTION: EXERCISES FOR POINT 1

1. Make a Joy List for Yourself

Take a page from your journal and number it from 1 to 50 or from 1 to 100 if you are feeling really ambitious. Then, write, as fast as you can, a list of things that you love to do, or that make you laugh, or that you enjoy doing with others. Now start finding ways to incorporate these things into your life.

2. Make a Joy List for Your Loved One

Do the same thing for your loved one. Write down as many things you can think of that he or she might enjoy. Even better, create the list with your loved one. Make it a game, something that the two of you can do together that will be fun and enjoyable.

3. Research Potential Pets.

Dog or cat? What breeds do you like? What will the costs be? Talk to your loved one and see how they might feel about having a pet. If they are in a live-in facility, find out what the center's policy is on pets. They may not allow residents to keep animals, but may allow visits from pets. If pets are not an option, consider plants or even stuffed animals.

4. Laugh Nine Times a Day

You can do it! Laughter is infectious and contagious in only the best of ways. And, laughter breeds more laughter. Once you get in the habit, you'll find ways to laugh all day.

Point 2: Relaxation, Meditation and Prayer

I chose relaxation, including meditation and prayer, as the second Point of my Brain Tune Up 9 Pt. System for caregivers because it is so vital to a caregiver's health and well-being.

Caregivers who don't deal effectively with stress can shorten their lifespan 4-8 years.[18] Or, even die before the loved one they're caring for.[19]

That's not *you* of course, because you've bought this book and you are dedicated to following the recommendations. Which is a good thing, because right about now you are no doubt thinking, *but I don't have time to relax.*

But you must make time for it, because relaxation, meditation, and prayer are necessities in everyone's life, most especially yours and your loved one's.

Make sure to take time daily to relax and unwind. If you don't have a pet or intend to get one, take a bubble bath, get a massage, read an inspirational book, do deep breathing exercises, meditate, work with affirmations and/or commune with your Higher Power. Journal and follow-up with the visualization exercise we'll learn more about later in this chapter. Whatever relaxes *you* and brings *you* peace, *do it.*

I know, I know. You're too busy to relax! Let's see...Take some time out now to relax...Or...Lose that time later from your lifespan. Hmmm...

Relaxation, meditation and prayer *are* necessities in everyone's life, most especially yours and your loved one's. If you still feel you need to convince yourself or your family of the importance of relaxation, tell them that Dr. Bresky ordered it.

Now that I've convinced you, let's get on with it by first looking at caregiver stress.

CAREGIVER STRESS

Long-drawn-out caregiver related stress can severely affect your mental, as well as, physical well being. But stress is often insidious, because unless we collapse with exhaustion or explode in anger, you might not even realize how stressed out you are. Stress is constantly working inside you, causing physical problems such as diabetes, heart problems, and high blood pressure. It can also contribute to mental issues of depression and anxiety. The fact that stress can cause those problems probably doesn't surprise you. But stress also causes skin problems, asthma, and arthritis. Amazing, isn't it, to think how being stressed out can have so many bad effects on the body? Statistics say that upwards of 75% to 90% of visits to the doctor are caused by stress.[20]

The chronic, unrelenting stress of providing care for someone is known as "caregiver syndrome" and once this "stress button" is pushed, we start to drown in a pool of the stress hormones adrenaline and cortisol.

Stress produces cortisol, which blocks glucose from entering brain cells. It is well known that cortisol shrinks the hippocampus, which is the initial memory forming site in the brain. It is also known that people who meditate have a larger hippocampus. Sometimes people turn to substances such as drugs or alcohol to relax. Unlike meditation, which takes a bit of discipline to master but has demonstrated relaxation effects, drugs and alcohol are easy to reach for but only make the problem worse. Contrary to common knowledge, drugs and alcohol actually end up stressing the body more, and this, as we have seen, causes more problems.[21] In this chapter, I'll show you how to replace stressful, self-defeating habits with relaxing, uplifting ones, so you too can increase your hippocampal volume.

I'll also give you pointers to help your loved ones relax, as well as ideas for engaging in relaxing, yet social time together. This will allow you to start combining Points and sharing Points with others, which makes this program easy and fun.

Being stressed makes everyone irritable. Remember, no one can stress you or make you irritable without your permission. Refuse to give permission to anyone, including yourself! When stressful or irritable thoughts or feelings arise, take a few deep breaths and think of ways to solve any challenges you're experiencing. Even taking the smallest steps can get you moving in a positive direction.

Is the stress I'm feeling manageable?

When are you dealing with manageable stress, and when should you seek help? Everyone deals with some level of stress every day. Ideally, you've come up with coping mechanisms to assist you in dealing with it. If you have an angry outburst for no reason, you may realize you are stressed and do something to relax. So, too, when stress is overwhelming you, your body will tell you—as long as you listen. Common symptoms of anxiety and stress overload include difficulty concentrating, and trouble sleeping. You may even lose your appetite. Physical indications are headaches, stomach aches, or a pounding heart. Emotional indicators may be panic attacks, or feeling overwhelmed to the point that you can't get any work done.

We all experience some variations on these symptoms from time to time. Let's face it, modern life is full of stress. But when any of these symptoms start to interfere with your daily life and activities, you might be stressed to the point of danger.

Anxiety causes every worry, large and small, to become a huge, looming obstacle. Every event is a crisis or a disaster. You've heard the phrase, "drama queen." Well, it's a safe bet that many drama queens are actually dangerously stressed out!

Another way that anxiety and stress manifests is as depression. Life can be overwhelming and you feel so stressed about it that you simply pull back. Nothing seems worth doing or getting involved in.[22] Amazingly, images taken of brains of people who have suffered stress or depression for many years show a significant loss of brain tissue.[23]

CONTROLLING AUTOMATIC RESPONSES

Once your body gets used to dealing with life as if everything is a crisis, it can get into a rut. Then it arms itself and starts to perceive nearly every event as a potential crisis, even if it is just common occurrence. The smallest thing sends you off into the stratosphere of anxiety. But these kinds of reaction can be prevented. Start by learning to assess a so-called crisis. Ask yourself:

- Is this really a crisis?

- Do I need to react to it immediately?

- What steps can I take to deal with it?

- When is the appropriate time to take those steps?

- Where can I make changes?

- What should I simply accept as it is?

By focusing on these kinds of questions you are finding positive solutions instead of dwelling on negative thoughts. Negative thoughts tend to take hold of us and pretend to be truth, but when you take the time to think them through they rarely hold up.[24] Instead of imagining the worst that could happen, envision fairy tale endings. Whenever you catch yourself thinking about what you *don't* want to happen, change it intentionally to what you *do* want to see happen.[25]

All that said, let's avoid giving stress a completely bad rap. Stress isn't all bad. It exists for a reason. Stress is our bodies' built in response to danger.

Adrenalin raises our blood pressure and heart rate so we can run faster, jump higher or punch harder. Cortisol moves blood sugar from the brain to our muscles. We've all heard stories of people finding superhuman strength to perform heroic acts and save others in danger.

This happened recently in New York City subway station. A 20-year-old student, Cameron Hollopeter, had a seizure and fell on the tracks as a train bore down on him. The crowd watched in horror, but one of them, a 50-year-old man named Wesley Autry, jumped in to save the student. As his young daughters watched, Autry wrestled Hollopeter into a drainage ditch and threw his own body on top of the student. With less than two inches clearance, the train rolled over the top of them and both men survived.[26]

As you can see from the above story, our bodies are designed to deal with stress in extreme circumstances. This is part of our survival modes. But when we start experiencing stress at these levels on a constant basis with no relaxation to temper it, stress becomes a problem.[27]

In general, we don't need the adrenaline-pumping reaction described above on a day to day basis, but often our bodies mimic this process. With all the stimuli we face, our bodies often go into stress-reaction mode at the slightest instigation—especially when we have not learned to counter these reactions with relaxation. When the body perceives a threat, it moves to prevent cortisol from overwhelming the brain by releasing hormones to the adrenal glands. When the perceived threat is over, it reverses this process, bringing the body into homeostasis. Homeo-what? Homeostasis. This is the condition of metabolic balance between stimulating and relaxing chemicals in your body. If either one of these get out of whack, you're no longer in homeostasis. And this is called, you guessed it, stress.

You can see how stress has a detrimental effect not only on your body, but your brain as well. Stress impacts memory by creating an energy crisis in the brain's hippocampus. When stress threatens, blood glucose is diverted away from the brain, resulting in a lack of energy there. And with this diminished energy, the ability to form memories is affected. Scientists theorize that this is why some people do not remember a traumatic event—so much glucose was used dealing with the trauma that there was none left to form memories. It also explains why people who have lived lives full of stress lose the ability to form short-term memory.[28]

STRESS RELIEVERS

- Take control of your life. Don't let circumstances and events control you

- Accept circumstances and events beyond your control

- Know when you've done all that you can

- Learn to manage time more effectively

- Keep a positive attitude

- Describe stressful situations as "challenging" instead of "awful" or "hopeless"

- Get enough sleep. Your body needs to recuperate from stressful events (Point 4)

- Exercise. It's a wonderful way to reduce anxiety and channel nervous energy (Point 5)[29]

- Enjoy yourself and engage in pleasant social interactions (Point 1)

- Listen to relaxing music (Point 3)

- Learn and practice relaxation techniques (This Point)

Adopting the Brain Tune Up 9 Pt. System is a fun and easy way to reduce stress and live a happier, healthier life.

INTEGRATING RELAXATION, MEDITATION AND PRAYER INTO YOUR LIFE

Now that you understand how vital relaxation, meditation and prayer are, let's talk about how to integrate them into your life, the life of your loved one and the time you spend together.

First off, let's talk about *you*. Because of course you know by now that caring for others starts with caring for yourself.

To learn to relax, pay attention to your breathing. Slow, deep breathing that expands your abdomen brings energy to every part of your body. But few of us breathe like this consistently. To the contrary—often the optimal flow of our breathing is interrupted by our emotions. Think about the last time you were highly anxious about something, or pay attention the next time it happens. Odds are good that you tended to hold your breath in, and your voice will be higher in pitch. Conversely, when you are depressed, you might sigh a lot, and your voice will be lower in pitch.[30]
Anytime you notice a change in your voice or that your breathing is erratic, take a few slow, deep breaths. This will calm the stress reaction you are experiencing.

Figure out a time of day you can allocate as 'me' time every day. Maybe a few minutes when you first wake up or before you go to bed would be a great start. It is important to create time to do this because there is a large body of research which cites the benefits of "me" time and meditation.

Studies have shown that spending as little as 20 minutes a day, focusing on your breathing—the most common of mediation techniques—or thinking soothing thoughts has beneficial effects. These include reducing pain, lowering blood pressure, and reducing anxiety.[31] A premise in meditation is that when your mind gets used to having an allocated time to quiet itself and relax, it does so quicker and more easily. This can also help with sleep (Point 4).

Meditation expands your brain, and not just in a metaphoric way but in a physical one. Researchers have found that the brains of people who have practiced meditation for many years actually have larger frontal cortexes. The frontal cortex is associated with attention and integrating emotion and thought. More studies are needed, but it is possible that meditation slows or reverses memory decline related to age.[32] That alone ought to convince you to take time to relax.

There are many different ways to meditate. Breathing exercises are an easy introduction to this ancient spiritual practice of quieting the mind and relaxing the body.

You'll find specific instructions for meditation in the exercise section at the end of this chapter. But for starters, try this:

To begin, find a peaceful spot. Turn off your phone and close the door to be free of interruptions. Remember, this is your time. The world can live without you for half an hour. Sit comfortably, either on a chair or on the floor (a chair is more comfortable for many beginning meditators). Train your mind to stay quiet. Know that you will become better with practice. Now pay attention to your breathing as you inhale and exhale. Breathe in and breathe out, simply observing your inhalations. If your mind wanders, bring it back to the breathing. You can either continue focusing on your breathing for the entire meditation session, or you can choose a specific meditation from the list at the end of this chapter.

AFFIRMATIONS

An activity that goes hand in hand with meditation is utilizing the power of affirmations. These are positive statements that evoke your desires and they operate on the principle that what you think and say actually creates your life. You've probably experienced this in various ways yourself. For instance, think of a time when you were happy and excited about life. On days like that, annoyances and irritations barely faze you. On the other hand, on days when you are depressed or sad, even cheerful thoughts or people may not perk you up. This is the power of your inner landscape.

It's not a big leap then, to ponder the power of what you might be saying to yourself. If you are constantly telling yourself how stupid, fat, and lazy you are, odds are good you'll act stupid, and be fat and lazy. The good news is that the reverse is true also. If you tell yourself how motivated, disciplined and energetic you are, those qualities will become part of you.

Intrigued? Why not put the power of affirmations to work for you. This section will give you some pointers on how to create powerful affirmations and ideas for how to most successfully use them. Let's get started.

Why use an affirmation?

Some research has shown that up to 75% of our self-talk is negative. That is an astounding figure. If you consider that your subconscious is acting on whatever you tell yourself, much of what you are putting out in the world is based on negative self-talk. Where does all this negativity come from? Our subconscious is like a sponge, absorbing everything it has ever heard. It's no wonder that destructive statements easily get lodged in our brains. But replacing those negative statements with a positive one can work wonders.

What is an affirmation?

An affirmation is a positive "I" statement expressed in the present. When writing an affirmation for yourself, you are writing a new script for your subconscious to put into play. Affirmations work on the principle of repetition. As you repeat the affirmation over and over again, eventually it will be imprinted on your subconscious and replace the old, negative scripts. Thus you don't even need to believe your affirmation for it to work!

Deciding what you want to change with affirmations

The first step in working with affirmations is deciding what you want to change. This may require a little detective work. Many of us are so accustomed to the negative chants in our head that we're not even aware of them. They are like "Musak" of the brain, a constantly repeating loop we've heard so often we don't pay attention. However, as they continually play, they continue to damage our lives. So first you must become aware of your negative statements, and then you can decide how to change it.

A common internal negative statement is "you're fat." Now, you may or may not need to drop a few pounds, but either way you don't want this nasty voice telling you how fat you are. Start to observe the negative things you tell yourself and write them down. In the next step you'll learn how to change them into a positive.

But don't stop with your current internal messages. You can also use affirmations to achieve goals and elevate your mood. Jot down a list of things you'd like to achieve. You might want to develop a more cheerful attitude, or feel more relaxed. Or maybe you'd like to have better self esteem. You can also use affirmations to move yourself to action. If you have always wanted to try your hand at art, design an affirmation around that. Or if you really do feel that you'd like to let go of a few pounds, write an affirmation for weight loss. The sky is the limit where affirmations are concerned. They are useful for just about anything you want to accomplish.

Writing the affirmation

When writing an affirmation, you want to make it positive, of course. And it is also important to write it in the present tense, as if you already embody the quality that you are affirming. Use emotion if possible and appropriate. You can also add your name to the statement for some extra oomph. Examples of affirmations for the goals listed above might be:

I, (insert name), am letting go of extra weight easily and effortlessly

I am cheerful and relaxed about life.

I make time to play with art.

I am confident in every situation I find myself in.

I care for my mother (or other loved one) in a relaxed, happy manner.

Are you starting to get the picture? Designing your own affirmations is a fun activity that can energize and inspire you.

Also note that you can find examples of affirmations in many books and on many websites. You can either use these affirmations as is, or modify them to better suit your needs. Authors who work with affirmations include Louise Hay, Florence Scovel Shinn, and Shakti Gawain.

Using your affirmations

Now that you have written your affirmations, find a way to collect them. You can write your affirmations in a small spiral notebook or on index cards. It doesn't matter what format you choose to collect them in, but it is helpful to write them down so that you'll have a record of what you are working on.

The most common way to use affirmations is to say them repeatedly, out loud. You can spend time using affirmations as a part of your "me" or meditation time. It is also beneficial to look in the mirror while you are saying them. Remember to smile while you watch yourself say them! Some people actually like to write the affirmations repeatedly on a daily basis, too. As you go about your day, remember to repeat your affirmations to yourself. Stuck in traffic? Say your affirmations. Waiting in the doctor's office? Repeat your affirmations to yourself.

Affirmations are simple yet powerful tools that truly do work wonders. The key is, of course, that you must use them regularly.[33] Once you start to see the changes in your life, I predict you'll become as big a fan of affirmations as I am.

PET THERAPY

As mentioned in the previous chapter, pet therapy is a wonderful way to relax and works for people in all stages of cognitive decline. Don't forget that it also works wonders for caregivers.

AROMATHERAPY

What is aromatherapy? It is exactly what it sounds like—using wonderful aromas as therapy for the body, mind and soul. Some of the therapies that aromas are used for include reducing anxiety and promoting relaxation, modifying moods, and easing tiredness. They have also been used successfully as a digestive aid, to help women in labor, and to alleviate the side effects of chemotherapy.

Aromas are disseminated via essential oils and can be added to the bath, infused throughout a room, or applied directly to the skin. Some of the aromas used are rose, Neroli, lavender, peppermint or lemon. But that is just the tip of the iceberg— there are a wide variety of readily available scents that you can try. As a matter of fact, there are over 150 of them!

Let's look at essential oils in depth for a moment. One of the reasons they are so powerful is that these oils are distilled from nature. They can be extracted from flowers, seeds, bark, grass, or fruit. These extractions have various qualities, including pain relief, anti-viral, anti-depressant, and anti-inflammatory benefits.[34]

Scientists are now beginning to study the effects of aromatherapy on dementia sufferers, and the results are promising. One study looked at the impact of using essential oils to lessen agitation in Alzheimer's patients. It used both inhalation and topically applied oils. The results showed a high incidence of participants completing the study (itself a rarity) and agitation declined markedly. One advantage of using aromatherapy with dementia patients is that it is still effective even if the person's sense of smell is compromised, which the case is often. The oils affect the body through substances called terpines, which are absorbed through the lungs and eventually released to the brain.[35]

Lavender is an excellent essential oil to begin with, as nearly everyone enjoys its smell. Other good oils to start with are Bergamot and Ylang Ylang. All three of these oils may exude a calming, relaxing effect.

- To aid your loved one's sleep, try Lavender, Rose, Neroli, Geranium, or Jasmine.

- To increase appetite, use Coriander, Clove, Cinnamon, Cardamom, Lemon, Lime, Nutmeg, Black Pepper, Orange, Grapefruit, or Ginger.

- To evoke memories, use Rosemary, Basil, Cardamom, or Black Pepper.

You might also want to use some of the essential oils yourself, either through inhalation, or infusing them into your home. Oils that promote happiness might be useful. Try Lavender, Bergamot or Ylang Ylang.[36]

Remember that applying cream-based essential oils to your loved one will give you the opportunity to utilize massage and this is also a great stress reliever. Massage has also been shown to reduce agitation in dementia patients.

OTHER IDEAS FOR RELAXATION

Enjoy Nature

Being in nature and listening to its sounds can be deeply relaxing, but this isn't always possible in our daily lives. To mimic these sounds, consider using recordings of ocean waves, a babbling brook, or rainfall in the forest.[37] You can purchase nature sound CDs or DVDs to play for yourself and/or your loved one.

Or, if possible, go on a nature walk.[38] Taking a nature walk combines relaxation (This Point) and exercise (Point 5), and, if you can do it with your loved one, social interaction (Point 1).

Sounds, Tones, and Mantras

We are musical beings, attuned to sounds, and our entire energetic system is influenced by all tones and frequencies, both negatively and positively.[39]

Mantras are often used in meditation for their sonic vibrational qualities. This makes music another wonderful way to relax. Listen to meditation and relaxation recordings if they soothe and calm you and/or your loved one. You can purchase audio recordings that combine relaxation instructions with soothing musical selections.

While many of us enjoy listening to these meditations CDs, others would prefer to relax to music. Soothing options include Native American music featuring flutes or drums, or perhaps something with a Celtic influence.[40] Whatever relaxes and soothes you and/or your loved one is the right choice. You can combine music with many of the relaxation suggestions given in this chapter. Combining music with relaxation therapy is more effective than doing relaxation therapy alone. We'll look at music therapy in detail in the next chapter.

PRAYER

If your loved one can still practice their faith or religion and you are not opposed to joining them, do so. The experience can uplift and inspire you both. If your loved one can no longer attend the religious services they once enjoyed and you know what those were, reading them passages from scriptures of their faith may relax them and bring them peace. Praying together can also be deeply calming, soothing and relaxing.

For this purpose, I'd like to share a prayer with you, written by one of my patients, that you may enjoy reading to your loved one:

Lord, Teach Me How to Pray

By Robert Anderson

O Lord, teach me how to pray

And organize my wishes, so that

You will understand my thoughts

Open my lines of

Communication for me

To ask intelligently

My desires in prose

Dear Lord, gather the seeds of wisdom in my soul,

Lift the vines of your mercy,

So that my tongue can speak my thoughts

Gracious Lord, when I can't find the words today

You will have to read my heart.

Psalm 91:11

"For he will command his angels concerning you to guard you in all your ways."

By being a caregiver, God is giving you the opportunity to be one of his angels, an angel of action. I believe one of the most significant and purpose-filled deeds you can perform in life is to elevate the quality of another's life. An angel of action does just that!

PUT IT INTO ACTION: EXERCISES FOR POINT 2

1. List Stresses

Make a list of the situations in your life that most causes you stress. Once you have gotten good and upset about them, now take a look at the list and see if there are ways you can change them. For instance, if feeling as if you never have enough time is an issue, can you buy a time management book? Be proactive and creative in looking for ways to deal with stress.

2. List Stress Relievers

Go back to the section on stress relievers and think about things you might like to do. Also refer to the Joy List you created earlier. Does window shopping always relax you? Write it on your list. Do you crave a massage? Make a note of it. The idea is to have a list of things you know will soothe you.

40

The next time you do have a free moment, you can easily refer to your list and choose a stress reliever instead of just plopping down in front of the television.

3. Schedule Me or Meditation Time

Meditation is the mother of all stress-busters. Take advantage of this simple technique. You'll find breathing techniques to get you started below. Once you make meditation a regular habit, you'll feel the benefits. The trick is in making it a regular habit. Schedule a regular time for it. Some people enjoy meditating first thing in the morning, while others prefer to practice it right before they go to bed. If neither of these times work for you, try taking a break at lunch time. Experiment until you find a regular time you can commit to.

4. Breathing Exercises

I've gathered a varied collection of breathing exercises for you to work with. You'll find that you enjoy some better than others, and that some of them work best in specific situations. Have fun with them; experiment.

Deep Breathing

Inhale and feel your abdomen extend while visualizing it filling up with air. Then slowly exhale as much air as possible, working to expel even the last little bits of it. Place your hand on your abdomen so that you can feel your stomach expanding and contracting.

Rhythmic Breathing

If you are having a stressful moment, or feeling anxious, rhythmic breathing can calm you quickly. As with deep breathing, the goal is to get your inhalations and exhalations to an unhurried pace. Do this by slowly counting to five as you inhale and then counting to five as you slowly exhale. After you've mastered the count of 5, see if you can draw it out even longer, perhaps even to the count of 10.

Visualizing the Breath

As before, begin by taking slow, deep breaths, feeling your abdomen expand and contract with air. Now add some mental imagery to it. Picture a deep sense of ease and relaxation entering your body every time you exhale. Picture all the stress and anxiety of the day leaving the body as you exhale. The visualization gives your relaxation a bit of extra oomph.

Muscle Relaxation

Relaxing the muscles as you breathe helps ease physical tension. It can also be an excellent way to focus if you have trouble with your mind wandering.

Breathe deeply. Now you are going to go through your entire body and tense and un-tense each major group of muscles. Start with your feet. Tense your left foot and hold it for a second or two. Now un-tense. Repeat with your right foot. Now continue all the way up your body, tensing and un-tensing each set of muscles.

Affirmation Breathing Exercise

Customize the above breathing exercises with whatever thoughts bring *you* the most peace and happiness. You can also adapt this exercise for use with positive affirmations.[41]

POINT 3: TUNES Rx

What is Tunes Rx? It is my take on Music Therapy, which we'll discuss in just a moment. But first, let's take a look at the beneficial effects of music.

Listening to music causes a person's breathing to slow and deepen, and this is a great weapon in the battle against stress. While you are engrossed in listening to music, your heart rate may also decrease, another aspect of stress relief. Music decreases the production of cortisol and adrenaline[42] and increases production of serotonin.[43]

Everyone has different tastes in music. What may be relaxing and soothing to you may sound jangly and discordant to the next person. The one thing studies have found that generally always works for relaxation is music that is played live. Keep this in mind when making your musical selections. Obviously, you can't head out to a concert every time you need to relax. But you can buy CDs of live performances.[44] If you sing or play music yourself, make sure to make time to do so. If you can sing or play music for your loved one, definitely do that.

Tunes Rx is an easy Point to use. You can listen to music in the car, while walking or even while doing chores, thanks to MP3 players. Tunes Rx is also an easy Point to combine with other Points. In order to fully understand Tunes Rx, let's first take a look at Music Therapy.

Music Therapy

What, exactly, is music therapy? It is music that is actually prescribed to a patient and this prescription may be used for a variety of effects, including spiritual, physical, and emotional aspects. Who, then, prescribes music therapy? It will be ordered by a doctor, or psychologist or even a social worker, and its use will be overseen by a music therapist. If you think that sounds like the sort of job one can just decide to do on a whim, think again. Music therapists study in rigorous programs to learn their profession.

Music therapy differs from the traditional study of music in that the point of it is not to develop musical skills such as learning to play the piano. The point of music therapy is to positively impact the patient's health. The focus can be on emotional, physical or social health.

Music therapists use what they call "musical interventions" (sounds lovely, doesn't it?) based on their studies of how music affects people's behavior. They will consider individual goals for each patient in developing their musical interventions.[45]

Music Therapy Goal Areas include:

- Cognitive skills

- Motor skills

- Emotional well-being
- Communication
- Social skills[46]

Music therapy intervention helps patients to:

- Create constructive changes in mood
- Create positive emotional states
- Support relaxation
- Demonstrate coping skills
- Encourage positive thoughts
- Encourage positive emotions
- Boost self awareness
- Encourage self-expression
- Encourage healthy social interaction
- Increase concentration
- Lengthen attention spans
- Increase problem-solving skills
- Increase decision-making skills
- Encourage and develop independence[47]

Examples of music activities and interventions include:

- Composing songs

- Instruction in piano playing. This can help patients to improve their fine motor skills.

- Moving to the music

- Singing[48]

- Talking about lyrics, what they mean and what feelings they evoke

- Discussing what images the music elicits

- Music improvisation

- Performing various kinds of music

- Active listening to music[49]

- Listening to music and reminiscing about what it brings up mentally[50]

A large body of research indicates that music therapy is a successful tool for many uses. Music therapy researchers have had good success working with Alzheimer's patients, for instance. Music therapy helped them to become more cooperative, less disruptive, and sleep better. These results came from therapy sessions of 30 minutes every day, five days a week.[51]

TUNES Rx

I've adapted these concepts of music therapy into my own program called Tunes Rx. With Tunes Rx, I'll give you suggestions and ideas that benefit both you and your loved one, no matter what stage of cognitive decline your loved one is in, or what level of stress you must deal with.

Tunes Rx will show you how to add music to your life, to your loved one's life, and to the time you spend together. Tunes Rx will enhance you and your loved one's ability to learn, inspire and uplift your spirits, and relax and calm you when you're stressed and agitated. It's an easy and fun way to improve *both* of your lives.

Music is an essential component of the human experience. Did you know that every single culture on earth has developed music in some form or another? No less a leader than Napoleon Bonaparte sang the praises and the power of music. He is quoted as saying, "Give me control over he who shapes the music of a nation, and I care not who makes the laws."[52]

Legends, myths and stories through the ages tell of music's magical abilities.[53] One biblical story tells of King Saul's depression and how David played the harp for him in order to ease it.[54] Shamans in many native cultures utilize the vibrational power of drumming, toning, and using other vocal emanations to invoke healing and set the mood for ceremonial rites.[55] The idea for using music as therapy actually reaches far back in history, with the ancient Greek philosophers mentioning it in their writings.[56]

In The Anatomy of Melancholy, a scholarly medical tome from the 17th century, Robert Burton wrote about the positive effects that music and dance had on treating depression, or what was then called melancholia.[57]

These days we hear and read much about the mind-body connection and how important it is to encourage and honor it. Listening to music is one way to do this and balance all aspects of a whole person.

Music therapy has been proven to have beneficial healing effects on the nervous, endocrine and immune systems.[58] Please note that when I talk about healing in this way, I am not necessarily talking about curing. Music therapy is used along with traditional medicine, as an additional healing modality.[59]

Music can be used to:

- Regulate and slow heartbeat, blood pressure and the pulse, which in turn eases stress and tension.

- Ease pain

- Reduce pain medication dosages by increasing endorphin levels

- Reduce stress hormone levels

- Give the immune system a boost

- Stimulate digestion and boost metabolism

- Ease effects of chemotherapy such as vomiting and nausea[60]

Studies have also shown that music actually alters brain patterns. Luckily, listening to music alters brain patterns in a positive way, improving depression, for instance.[61] One study found that it reduced depression by 25%. Studies have also found listening to music can alleviate chronic pain by up to 21%.[62]

Why does music therapy work so well to ease depression and pain? Researchers believe at least part of the answer lies in the simple principle of diversion. Quite simply, listening to music takes your mind off the pain. We've all had the experience of putting on upbeat music to wipe away our blues, and science now confirms our instincts.[63] If you or your loved one are feeling low, play some cheerful music that takes your mind off your troubles.

TYPES OF MUSIC TO USE

What should you play? Anything you or your loved one enjoy listening to. I personally recommend Mozart's Piano Concerto #21. For reasons I'll discuss in detail later, this selection is extremely therapeutic.

If that's not in your library, think of something *you* want to hear. Does Bob Marley get you jammin'? Put on some reggae, mon. Show tunes blow up your skirt? Liza will surely work. Tongue in cheek songs more your style? Randy Newman is good for a smile. Does disco make you want to dance? Surely that Bee Gees CD is somewhere in your stack. Do you like bluegrass, polka, salsa, or country? Crank it up!

The following recommendation may sound counter-intuitive, but sometimes when a person is deeply depressed, cheerful music may not do the trick. Instead, match the music to their mood and play slower, sadder music. This may actually help to alleviate depression by validating it. One person described it this way: "When one hears sad music composed by a man who suffered, as did Chopin, Beethoven and Tchaikovsky, one feels that I am seconded, and in feeling the beauty of that music I forget I am not well."[64]

For great music to second your sadness grab some of the classical composers listed in his quote.

Not what you had in mind? How about some good old fashioned blues? Country music can work too, or any sad ballad for that matter. Whatever speaks to *your* pain and helps *you* transcend it, may that music play on. Studies have shown that putting relaxing, soothing music on goes deep and eases the root causes of mood disorders, which may include anxiety, anger, or depression. This may be because listening to music allows you to slow your body functions and your thoughts and gets you to focus on your feelings.[65]   The beauty of this is that adding Tunes Rx to your life is easy. It is probably the easiest Point to integrate into your life. For instance:

- Combine Tunes Rx with physical exercise (Point 5)

- Combine Tunes Rx with mealtime (Point 6)

- Combine Tunes Rx with social time (Point 1)

- Combine Tunes Rx with your "me" time and deep breathing exercises (Point 2)

- Combine Tunes Rx and the time you spend with your loved one (Points 1 and 9)

- Combine Tunes Rx with combinations of Points

There is no "one size fits all" music that will please everyone. It may take you a minute to find Tunes Rx that works for both you *and* your loved one.

The Tunes Rx for you or your loved one when you're in a funk will probably be different than the Tunes Rx for you or your loved when you need motivation or want to be soothed and relaxed. Different Tunes Rx are required for different moods, situations and goals.

Want to be inspired and empowered? Music and entertainment can help you boost your confidence and immediately alter your mood.[66]   Choose a musical selection that evokes feelings of courage, faith, and strength.[67] The kind of music that inspires these feelings in you may be completely different than the next person and that is fine.

Whatever uplifts and inspires *you* and your loved one play it. Upbeat music can be Tunes Rx during your day if you need stimulation. It will invigorate and recharge you.

We've all indulged in comfort food when we're feeling blue, but how about some comfort music? Why not indulge yourself in some oldies but goodies for your Tunes Rx? Studies have shown that listening to your favorite tunes from childhood or your teenage years is a comforting activity.[68] Studies show that even people with severe cognitive decline can remember and sing along with old, familiar tunes.[69] Put on songs your loved one knows and have a sing-a-long.

Tunes Rx serves many diverse purposes. It can also be used to urge originality and contemplation. Now that you understand the *many* benefits of Tunes Rx, make sure to incorporate it into your day, as well as the time you spend with your loved one. There's *always* time for Tunes Rx, because you can listen while doing other things. Play Tunes Rx in your car on the way to work, at home while you're fixing meals or cleaning, while you're relaxing before bed or while you're in the company of your loved one.

TUNES Rx AS A MOOD CHANGER

I've already told you music can work magic on your bad moods and help to relieve stress. One reason I get so excited about it is that music works on many levels at once.[70] Listening to music is a transcendent experience. What do I mean by this? Music can transport you from the chair you are sitting in to a whole different world in your mind. Through music, you can visit places you've been long ago, or create new places you'd love to travel to in your mind. Listening to music allows us to bypass the abstract, linear function of our brain and let it roam free. This is a deeply relaxing activity, and as you let the music wash over you, you may go through states of consciousness ranging from an expanded sensory threshold, to daydreaming, trance state, meditative state or into rapture.

These are the states of consciousness associated with deep relaxation and in any of them, you'll experience time differently, perhaps even losing track of it. People get so caught up in the music, they forget to worry about the clock! These relaxing states are excellent in relieving fear, pain, and depression.[71]

Music is one of the few experiences that touch people on many levels. You can play Tunes Rx while you're working, cooking dinner, cleaning, or going about any kind of day to day activities. You probably won't even realize it, but the music you have been playing will be reducing your stress level.[72] Few people don't enjoy listening to music, and it is nice to know that it is actually helping you at the same time you are having a pleasurable experience.

What is it about music that is soothing? Researchers theorize that it is the first thing we hear. When we are as yet unborn in our mother's womb, we are comforted by the soothing sound of our mother's heart, beating rhythmically. So it's no surprise that the beat of music takes us back to that wonderfully safe and serene time, at least somewhere deep in our psyche.[73]

Tunes Rx is also a *wonderful* way to decrease agitated behavior in people with cognitive decline.[74] It can help to balance both emotions and hormones as effectively as meditation and yoga.[75]

A great way to relax with Tunes Rx is to take an invigorating walk while listening to music on your MP3 player. Time your stride to the beat of the music, or get your breathing in sync with it. Play different tempos of music and see which one you like best. Have some fun! This will not only help to ease stress, but it will combine exercise (Point 5), relaxation (Point 2) *and* music (This Point!)

For a wonderful meditative experience, take a 20 to 30-minute Sound Break. Choose music that is relaxing to you and get into a comfortable position, either lying on the couch or sitting in a comfortable chair. Now just relax and let that slow beat surround you. Concentrate on the notes of the various instruments, and think about how slow and steady and deep your breathing is. One trick music therapists use is to listen for the silences between the musical notes.[76] Sounds a little funny, but it's a good way to prevent your linear mind from analyzing the music. All you have to do is breathe and let the music surround you. Ahhhh. What a wonderful way to take a break from the cares of the world!

If you are looking for particularly relaxing music, choose that which has a rhythm slower than 72 beats a minute. Why? This it the natural rhythm of the heart (remember all that time you spent listening to it in your mother's womb) and listening to music a bit slower will ease you down a notch.[77] (See more about the Sound Break in the exercise section at the end of this chapter.)

MOZART AND BAROQUE MUSIC

Whenever the proper sounds are experienced, an amazing left/right brain synchronization occurs.[78] This is one reason why I recommend classical music, which has approximately 60 beats per minute. This rhythm appears to motivate learning. It has also been shown to be useful in helping the brain to process and retain information.[79]

Studies have shown that playing some of Mozart's slower pieces can help students focus and pay attention.[80] You might want to try this for yourself or to help your loved one. At the very least, you'll enjoy listening to the music.

One very good reason to spend some time with Mozart is the beneficial effect it will have on your brain. Appreciating music activates listening skills. At least part of your brain has to concentrate to hear the beat of the music, as well as its tonal quality, rhythm and its underlying patterns. Listening skills contribute to the cognitive development of your brain.[81]

Not only do you listen to music, but you also feel it in your body. This is true for rock music with a heavy bass, which you can feel reverberating within, but it is also true for classical Baroque compositions. Baroque music actually helps you to physically relax. Why? Because your pulse and heart rate slow to match it's beat. Your body relaxes, and your brain follows suit, releasing hormones which in turn cause more relaxation. Researchers have a relatively easy time detecting such changes, because the physical responses are easily measured. Study after study has shown that the music of Mozart's era slows breathing, and decreases blood pressure. All of this contributes to an enhanced capability to learn.

Music also affects memory, and the effect is nothing but positive. The patterns of Baroque and classical music cause the brain to respond in special ways.[82]

We've all had the experience of hearing a snatch of music and being instantly transported to a pleasant memory. Research suggests that music can have this same effect on patients with dementia. Music can also help them experience positive emotions and boost their self-esteem.[83] Just as Mozart's music has been shown to have beneficial effects on the attention spans of adults with healthy brains, this same effect has been noted in Alzheimer's patients. Some researchers think it may even be useful in keeping Alzheimer's at bay. Scientists at Loyola University in Chicago uncovered the fascinating finding that orchestra musicians who played their instruments throughout their lives were less likely to develop Alzheimer's.[84]

Studies like these are why I am so bullish on Tunes Rx! When we combine listening to music (this Point) with cognitive stimulation such as lifelong learning or solving crossword puzzles (Point 8), healthy social relationships (Point 1), we start to make real progress in the fight against dementia. All of these activities can help to keep the brain healthy as it ages.[85]

The great thing about music is that everyone can listen to it. Everyone can find some kind of music that they like, whether it is classical, folk, rap, or rock. Listening to music is an activity that people of diverse backgrounds and ages can enjoy and as such, it makes a great tool with Alzheimer's patients.

This was shown recently in a study done by Canadian psychologists. They tested patients with severe dementia on their ability to appreciate music. The results were surprising and gratifying. Even those patients who had such advanced cases of dementia that they couldn't communicate well were able to recognize music.[86] Even patients with severe dementia could sing songs from their childhood. Every time the music played, these patients happily sang along. Evidence is starting to accumulate that musical abilities are located in parts of the brain not affected by Alzheimer's.[87] Your loved one with Alzheimer's (or any advanced cognitive decline) would most likely enjoy more music in their environment.

Music can assist dementia sufferers with sundowning, which most often appears in the late afternoon or evening. (See Point 5 for a discussion of sundowning.) It can also help if they get agitated at other times of the day, or need to be transported somewhere. Try playing music for them or even humming one of their favorite tunes. This can have a soothing, calming effect.[88]

Alzheimer's specialist Gayatri Devi, M.D., has used music therapy extensively for Alzheimer's patients and proscribes it often. "We know that music therapy provides real benefits for both Alzheimer's patients and their caregivers," she says. "... playing the patient's favorite music improves his sleep; playing it when he's bathing decreases his agitation and hitting behavior and increases his compliance; playing it at mealtime may improve his appetite."[89]

Researchers are getting excited about the possibilities of using music to assist Alzheimer's patients, and reports are beginning to come in of great successes. A Japanese study showed that the speech in 6 out of 10 Alzheimer's patients improved after they participated in music therapy. An important finding of this study was that the improvement remained after the therapy was finished.[90]

Another study found that Alzheimer's patients slept better after music therapy. The improved sleep pattern lasted for six weeks, and was measured by the patient's melatonin levels. The above-mentioned Dr. Devi says, "Incorporating music therapy into a patient's life is a no-brainer, considering that it's so inexpensive and that these studies show beneficial effects and no negative effects."[91]

These studies give ample evidence that Tunes Rx can be extremely beneficial for the person with Alzheimer's or cognitive decline.

When using Tunes Rx for a person with Alzheimer's or severe cognitive decline:

- Choose familiar songs, perhaps from their childhood or other happy time

- Don't use loud music

- Play only music, shutting off other sensory stimulates such as TV. Also close the door and draw the drapes. This will help the patient focus on the music.

- Use music to set a mood. Quiet tunes are appropriate for bedtime, while cheerier songs can be played earlier in the day or for special events.

- Sing along! Get into the swing of the music and encourage the patient to sing, clap, hum, or even play an instrument.

- Couple music with family photos to encourage good memories.[92]

- Use music as a way to enhance communication.[93]

Music can be a mind-expanding activity for Alzheimer's patients with subliminal messages positively engaging them.[94] Oliver Sacks, Neurologist and author, who teaches at my alma mater Albert Einstein College of Medicine, discovered advanced Parkinson's patients have an "extraordinary" response to music. "These people who couldn't utter a syllable or take a step sometimes could sing beautifully and could dance, and music seemed to let them flow in a way they couldn't do in any other circumstances," he says. "We are an intensely musical species, even people who say they are unmusical and tone deaf. There's a remarkable amount of the brain that's concerned with processing music, far more than is concerned with processing language, and I think it's very much part of the human state."[95]

Patients with other types of brain disabilities have also benefited from music therapy. Researchers studied recent stroke victims for six months. They learned that daily exposure to music improved verbal memory by 60%, and led to a 17% rise in performance on tasks that required concentration. A control group listened to audio books and showed only 18% improvement.[96]

As you can see from all of these studies and benefits, Tunes Rx is an amazing Point. Use it for yourself and your loved one as much as possible. After Tunes Rx sessions, you'll witness your loved ones in calmer, better moods.

Incorporating music into your life, your loved ones life, and the time you spend together will improve the quality of *both* your lives dramatically!

Environmental Sounds and White Noise

Besides music, there are also other sounds that may enrich your life and the life of your loved one. Most of us who are urban dwellers are quite used to the environmental noises that are a part of our lives. However, some sounds can upset patients with dementia, whereas we might not even notice them. The sound of a siren could elicit fear or shock, and the cry of a baby could cause anxiety.[97]

If you notice such environmental noises affecting your loved one, you might want to consider the use of white noise. White noise masks all sound frequencies, as it is made up of random monotonous noise of equal power across the whole audio spectrum. White noise works because it masks all sounds without adding new sounds to the environment.

You may have inadvertently experienced white noise if you've ever slept with a fan on, or used one in a bathroom. The steady drone of the fan masks any other noises in the room or outdoors.[98]

When you need to block sounds in your environment, or the surroundings of your loved one, white noise is the ticket. It's a great choice for patients who get agitated easily. You can use something as simple as a fan, or invest in a white noise machine, which has the advantage of not cooling the air. White noise machines often play the sounds of a babbling brook or the gentle pounding of ocean waves.

Use White Noise if Your Loved One:

- Exhibits physically aggressive behaviors

- Exhibits verbally aggressive behaviors

58

- Repeats verbal sounds

- Paces

- Constantly handles objects[99]

You might also try playing instrumental Tunes Rx that's calm, soothing and repetitive as well. If you or your loved one has trouble sleeping, Tunes Rx is a beneficial solution. (We'll talk much more about sleep in the next chapter.)

Combining Tunes Rx (this Point) with suggestions from Relaxation, Meditation and Prayer (Point 2) will help facilitate you and your loved one's ability to enjoy and engage in a wonderfully *essential* part of life.

One of the easiest ways to fall asleep is to listen to Mozart's Piano Concerto #21. Mozart's music is good for any kind of Tunes Rx, including relaxation, the encouragement of sleep, and just plain pure pleasure. Even if you have never "gotten" or enjoyed classical music, I urge you to give it a try.

PUT IT INTO ACTION: EXERCISES FOR POINT 3

1. Experiment with Different Kinds of Music.

Downloading music from the internet makes this easy. You can buy one track cheaply and see how you or your loved one likes it. This is a great way to experiment with genres of music that you may not be familiar with.

2. Walk with Tunes Rx

Walking to music is wonderfully relaxing. Match your breath to the beat of the music, or take steps that match the rhythm of the beat. This can be fun and entertaining, as well as a healthy way to use Tunes Rx. Not to mention, you're Point combining!

3. Take a Sound Break

Instead of taking a coffee break, take a sound break. Get comfortable on a bed or a couch. Wear headphones if you like. Choose Tunes Rx with a slow rhythm, slower than the natural heart beat, which is about 72 beats per minute. Let the music surround you and fill you up completely. Breath slowly and fully and just allow yourself to enjoy listening to the music. This is a wonderfully relaxing treat.[100]

POINT 4: SLEEP

Sleep is the next Point of my Brain Tune Up 9 Pt. System because sleep is *essential* to *everyone's* health and well-being, and something a lot of caregivers and their loved ones find elusive.

Remember, if you're tired, angry and depressed, you're not going to be in any shape to provide service to the ones you love. Sleep is one of those funny things that you don't realize how much you miss until you experience a full, restful night of it. A sleep deprived person will feel tired and moody, but only when she finally gets a good night's sleep will she remember, *oh that's what it feels like to be rested.*

It will come as no surprise to you to learn that sleep is necessary to human survival. That's because it is the most basic of our body's natural cycles. Our bodies are keyed to biological rhythms, and sleep is no different. Some of the functions that these natural rhythms regulate include breathing, digestion, body temperature, and blood pressure.

Our sleep cycles are controlled by two things: One inner, the brain, and one outer, the Earth, as it turns from day to night.

Sleep has a far more important function than simply satisfying your drowsiness. While you're snoring away at night, your body is hard at work. Doing what? Repairing and revitalizing organs, for one thing. Sleep also insures that your immune system will work properly. Same with the nervous system. Imagine a whole crew of workers scurrying about to fix problems with your body while you sleep and you'll get an idea how important sleep is to your health.[101]

BENEFITS OF SLEEP

You've probably had the experience of not sleeping well for a few nights and then finally getting a good night's sleep. You wake up the next day feeling refreshed and happy. And only then do you realize what a difference a good night's sleep makes. Sleep not only makes you feel better, it makes you look better, too. Ponder the image of someone who's not slept well—saggy eyelids, puffy under-eye skin, dark shadows on the skin. There's no doubt that a well-rested person simply looks better than one who is not sleeping at night.[102] Those are all pretty good reasons to find ways to ensure a good night's sleep for both you and the person you are caring for.

Why is this? Scientists think it might have to do with growth hormones which flourish with sleep. Growth hormones, not surprisingly, are what help us to maintain a youthful look. The bad news is that their levels drop from age 20 on. The best way to push the levels higher is through sleep.[103]

Sleep is not only vital for your appearance, but also your brain. Studies suggest that sleep-deprived people can't learn information as well as those who have had plenty of sleep (and anyone who has ever sat in a classroom after being out too late the night before can attest to this). Not only that, but researchers also believe that sleep assists the brain in strengthening what it has learned.[104]

HOW MUCH SLEEP?

You've probably read or heard that you should get at least 7 or 8 hours of sleep a night for health. This is something that most sleep experts do agree on.

However, sleep issues rise as we age, and it may become difficult to get this many hours of sleep in. Many older people have trouble with falling asleep and staying asleep, with sleeplessness starting to be a problem at ages as young as 30. As we age, one big problem is time spent attempting to fall asleep. By age 60, many report problems sleeping the night through, and by this age, 30% of people report trouble with sleeping. Most sleep medication prescriptions are written for older adults.

Because changes in memory also occur as we age, researchers are looking into possible links between memory and sleep, or lack thereof. Studies are investigating memory declines and high rates of insomnia and other problems with sleep.[105]

We humans experience two different kinds of sleep:

- **REM** (Rapid Eye Movement) sleep, is so named because its hallmark is short bursts of rapid eye movement. It is during REM sleep that you'll be most likely to dream.

- **NREM** (Non-rapid Eye Movement) is the deepest sleep you experience when delta waves predominate. Delta waves are the slowest brain waves.

Both kinds of sleep are needed for the health of the brain and the body, and in the course of the night, your body will alternate between the two. Researchers have also learned that each kind of sleep is crucial to different types of memories:

- REM sleep helps with procedural memory (how to *do* things like learn to ice skate, write a story, or ride a skateboard).

- NREM sleep is associated with declarative memory (how to *recall* things, such as facts you might remember for a test.)[106]

All of us have gotten by with a few late nights, so it is obvious that we can make due without the proper amount of sleep. However, depriving yourself of sleep over the long haul can have detrimental effects on the brain and the body.

CAUSES OF SLEEP DEPRIVATION

Many kinds of sleep deprivation, including insomnia, can be caused by physical ailments, such as pain or difficulties in breathing. Also at fault may be the medications people take for these problems. Many commonly prescribed pills list sleeplessness as a side effect, and this is also true of over-the-counter medication. Even those anti-histamines you take can cause sleep problems! People under treatment for cancer, arthritis, and heart disease, to name only a few, may be taking medication that causes sleep disorders. Check with your doctor if you suspect your pills may be causing problems.

Another cause is depression, which studies have shown to be the cause of up to 15% to 20% of reported insomnia cases.[107] As stated earlier, sleeping problems are often an indicator of depression.

Another common cause of sleep problems is anxiety. This is somewhat of a vicious circle, because anxiety can cause
64

insomnia and insomnia can cause anxiety. Either way, it's clear the two can go hand in hand. Researchers have learned that people with ongoing insomnia are at higher risk of developing generalized anxiety disorder[108] which is an abnormal or excessive worry about daily life.

People with insomnia not only tend to be more anxious, they also produce more stress hormones, and this in turn tunes up their bodies to a highly energized state which makes sleep more difficult. Just as we saw with the cycle of anxiety, lack of sleep then causes more stress, the same vicious circle.[109]

Empty your stress load before trying to sleep. Deal with worries and distractions several hours before bed. If you're having problems you should journal about them.

If you're going over everything you need to do, make an action list for the next day, so you don't think about things all night and can offload all your anxieties before bed.

EFFECTS OF SLEEP DEPRIVATION

In our hectic, 24-hour world, many people find getting a good night's sleep to be something they last experienced as a baby. We've seen that a high percentage of adults over age 60 struggle with sleep issues. But it is a problem for adults of all ages. A recent National Sleep Foundation survey reported 60% of adults of all ages have difficulty falling asleep more than one night a week.[110]

Serious sleep disorders have been linked to hypertension, heart attack, and stroke. Research shows the 24% of middle-aged adults who slept less than 5 hours a night developed high blood pressure, compared with 12% of their peers who slept 7 or 8 hours a night.[111]   High blood pressure is a major risk factor for heart disease, stroke and dementia, and doubles your Alzheimer's risk. Other physical problems associated with sleep disorders include a higher risk of obesity and diabetes.[112]

Results of Chronic Sleep Deprivation:

- Reduces the effectiveness of your metabolism and increases your appetite—no wonder sleep disorders are linked to obesity!

- Along the same lines, insomnia adversely affects your levels of leptin, which is what makes you feel full. As if that's not enough, it also increases the levels of the hormone that increases your hunger. It's a double whammy, waiting to make you overweight.

- Can make you crave sugary foods and carbs.

- Puts you at higher risk for diabetes.

- Affects mood.

- Affects memory.

- Affects concentration.

- Affects your ability to solve problems.

- Adversely affects the way you process food, including carbs.[113]

- Affects ability to hold your temper

- As we've seen, it increases stress[114]

- Increases depression and anxiety[115]

- Lowers motivation. It's hard to get motivated about just about anything when you're exhausted.

- Adversely affects reflexes, slowing them down

- Can cause you to make careless mistakes[116]

- Affects ability to make good decisions[117]

- Weakens the function of the immune system, making you vulnerable to disease

- Affects alertness, reducing it. This can cause traffic accidents and falls.[118]

Lack of sleep can affect your physical and cognitive skills to such a large degree that you're just as dangerous as a drunk driver, *without having a single drink!*[119] Not only that, but sleep deprivation can mimic other diseases. One study found that among young, healthy men, only 4 hours of sleep for 6 nights in a row was enough to create a temporary pre-diabetic state.[120]

Restless leg syndrome and sleep apnea are two common problems which cause difficulties in sleeping.[121] Sleep apnea, where breathing stops during sleep, can increase a person's risk for developing vascular dementia.[122] See your doctor if you experience either of these issues.

You can see from this long list of problems related to sleep deprivation that it is nothing to be treated lightly. If insomnia goes on for any length of time, it can impact every aspect of your life including health, work, relationships and your emotional state.[123]

SYMPTOMS OF INSOMNIA

You most likely know if you have insomnia. Symptoms include:

- Difficulty getting to sleep

- Difficulty staying asleep long enough to get rested[124]

- Waking often during the night

- Waking up too early and not being able to get back to sleep[125]

- Feeling tired when you wake or throughout the day[126]

If you have any of these problems regularly, please talk to your doctor. The brain heals itself every night, growing and forming new memories. Thus it's *vital* to get adequate sleep.

PROFESSIONAL HELP

Television is full of ads for prescription and non-prescription sleeping aids alike, which gives you an idea of how widespread the problem is. Because sleep problems are so common, these medications are widely prescribed. Always discuss taking any kind of sleeping pills with your physician—and this includes over-the-counter pills, too.[127]

Other alternatives to look into are light therapy and cognitive behavioral therapy.[128]

Cognitive Behavioral therapy may not have an immediately recognizable name, but it has been around for 40 years. This type of therapy helps people to retrain their thought patterns to ease psychological problems.[129] It looks at the person's ideas and expectations around sleep, and retrains them if they are erroneous. Examples would include working with appropriate age-related sleep goals, and looking at behavioral effects such as afternoon naps and exercise.[130]

Some people have sleep problems because their circadian rhythms are off. Your circadian rhythm is essentially your internal clock, and it regulates when you feel awake and when you feel sleepy (thank your circadian rhythm for that drowsiness you feel mid-afternoon). One way that your inner clock gets set is by exposure to bright light, which is why many people wake earlier in the spring and summer and sleep later in winter. If your circadian rhythms are off, light therapy can help reset them. Light therapy resets the internal clock by exposure to bright light, most often using a light box to do so.[131]

Both of these therapies have proven helpful for sleep problems, and are well worth checking out.

One more suggestion is to look into melatonin, which is readily available at health food stores. As we age, the hormone melatonin, which is associated with sleep, decreases.[132] Replacing melatonin with a natural over-the-counter preparation can reduce the effects of this decrease.

GOOD SLEEP HABITS

If you are having difficulty sleeping, the first thing to do is to check out your sleeping habits. You may have formed some bad ones without even knowing it. There are a variety of things you can try that may have a big impact on your sleep patterns or those of your loved one.

1. Follow a schedule. One of the simplest things you can do to ensure better sleep is to get in bed and wake up at a consistent time every day. Keep it within two hours for best results.[133] **It is best to sleep between 11 PM and 7 AM.** These are the hours when your brain heals itself and memories form; take advantage of them!

2. Devise a consistent sleep plan. Do the same thing every night before you go to bed. Many people enjoy reading

69

for a few minutes before turning out the light. Some people take a bath or shower, and others enjoy a cup of tea or a light snack. Doing the same thing each night tells your body it is time for sleep.[134]

This is similar to the concept of setting aside the same time of day for your relaxation, meditation and prayer (Point 2) so that your mind will quiet itself more easily and quickly. In fact, prior to bed is an *excellent* designated time for meditation or personal time. Slow, deep breathing before bed, or once you're in bed, helps you sleep.

Consider using your favorite relaxation techniques from Point 2. If you wake during the night, again, use your favorite relaxation techniques to fall back asleep. Or don't forget the soothing effects of using Tunes Rx, such as Mozart's Piano Concerto #21, before bedtime.

3. Make your bedroom peaceful. Be certain that the room where you sleep is quiet and not too bright. Darkness is conducive to sleep because light affects the sleep cycle.[135] Use shades or curtains or heavy drapes to ensure darkness. Be aware that even the light from a clock radio can be disruptive.[136]

Lower the volume in the surroundings.[137] Consider using white noise, as mentioned earlier, if it is impossible to control the level of noise around your loved one or yourself.

Pay attention to room temperature. We've all experienced tossing and turning due to being too hot at night, or conversely, huddling in the fetal position to try to get warm. The most conducive temperature for sleep is between 60-65 degrees Fahrenheit.[138]

Check out your mattress. You may be sleeping on an old one that no longer serves you. Buy a supportive mattress that satisfies your sleeping needs, whether you prefer soft or firm. You won't get a good night's sleep if you are sleeping on a mattress that is too soft or too firm for you. Just ask Goldilocks![139]

Buy luxurious bedding. The stores are full of beautiful, soft comforters and quilts, and pillows designed for side sleepers, back sleepers or stomach sleepers. Choose the right one for your style of sleep.[140]

4. Regulate eating and drinking before bed. Try not to eat a full meal before bed, as this can adversely affect sleep. Conversely, hunger can also make it difficult to sleep. Many people enjoy a snack before bed. Keep it small, though![141]

With respect to diet, eat small frequent meals during the day that are rich in protein and complex carbohydrates, like fruits and vegetables (Point 6).

Confine caffeine to the morning hours. Or better yet, banish it all together. This includes tea, coffee, and soda.[142]

To avoid nighttime urination problems, plan to drink most of your water earlier in the day.

Avoid alcohol or drink it sparingly. Many people think that alcohol helps you sleep but the opposite is true. While it may help you get to sleep faster, it can also cause wakefulness and insomnia.[143]

5. Exercise! You'll learn much more about good fitness in Point 5, but for now let me just mention that regular exercise will help you to sleep better, period. The only thing to be wary of is doing your exercise session too close to bedtime. This can make falling asleep difficult.[144]

Remember, you can always combine Points, too! Sex can be a *wonderful* way to get a little exercise (Point 5), have some fun (Point 1) and fall into a deep sleep (This Point!)

6. Use the bedroom for bedroom activities. Bedrooms are for sleep and sex. Doctor's orders. Do not get in the habit of using your bedroom to watch TV (there's nothing worse than watching the news right before bed), surfing the internet, or paying bills. Remember, sleep and sex only.[145]

7. Honor your body's natural cycles. One common mistake people make is going to bed when they think they should. Wait until you are truly tired. (This is one reason exercise is so good for sleep—it wears you out.) Don't take naps if you've not slept well the night before, as they will only make matters worse.[146]

8. Other sleep tips to consider. Don't smoke! You know it's bad for you, but it is also hard on your sleep patterns. Studies have shown that smokers are often bad sleepers. They have trouble falling asleep promptly and wake more often in the night.[147]

If you're having trouble falling sleep, wait 20 minutes. If you're still awake after that, get out of bed and go do something. Do your relaxation exercises, listen to Tunes Rx (Mozart anyone?). Another good trick is to do something boring to lull your brain to sleep. Try reading the manual for the new appliance you just bought. That ought to put you right to sleep.[148]

As much as we all love our animal companions and as wonderful as pet therapy is, don't sleep with animals in the same room *if* they disturb your sleep. [149] If they don't disturb your sleep, well then, that's a different story!

If your pets do disturb your sleep, however, keep them out of the bedroom at night. Make it up to them by giving them extra special "Good morning, I love you" time.

Finally, remember all the benefits to sleep and the problems that not getting enough of it can cause. Then when you are tempted to stay up late, it'll be easier to go to sleep instead.

Making sleep a consistent priority can give you a new lease on life.[150]

NAPS

What about naps to catch up on lost sleep or revitalize you during the day? If you had a sleepless night, try taking a short nap of no more than 45 minutes.

Having a nap for 30-45 minutes can be a good thing, helping you process information, feel refreshed and even ward off heart disease. Napping for an extensive period of time or having more than one nap during the day, however, can be a bad thing. It steals slumber from your nighttime rest.[151]

Naps, like everything else, require proper balance. A little nap can do you a world of good. An overly long nap, or a series of naps, will do more harm in the long run. That goes for you *and* your loved one. If you're a parent, you understand the concept! Who wants a wide awake baby at night? Who wants a wide awake *anyone* at night? You don't want your loved one with cognitive decline up and about at night, keeping you awake. And you don't want yourself wide awake at night, setting yourself up for a less than ideal next day!

If you're going to nap, midday, following lunch, is usually a good time. People who have traveled in Spain and other countries have experienced the tradition of midday siestas. Americans and the British frown on such "laziness" but many scientists believe that taking an afternoon siesta is actually the healthier option.

One recent study showed that an afternoon nap might help prevent heart disease. The results showed that those who slept 30 minutes at least 3 times a week had a 37% lower chance of a heart attack.[152]

Another study shows that naps, a habit enjoyed by Albert Einstein, John F. Kennedy, Ronald Reagan, Bill Clinton, Florence Nightingale, Winston Churchill, Lady Thatcher, the Duke of Wellington and so many others can have a good effect on increasing memory. Participants in the study were asked to memorize a list of words. Some got to take a nap before repeating back the words, and others didn't. Those who napped had a better memory for the words.[153]

While we sleep, our brain processes memories and researchers now think that this is of vital importance to the basic functions of the brain.[154]

Siesta anyone? As long as it is a short one, go for it.

SLEEP ISSUES FOR CAREGIVERS

Caregivers have their own special sleep challenges. Even though, as we now know, *caring for others starts with caring for yourself,* that's easy to forget when you love someone and are attending to their needs. Remember though, that if you're tired, angry and depressed how much service can you truly provide to the ones you love?

Also bear in mind that caregivers who don't take care of themselves run the risk of dying before the loved one they're caring for. And then who will take care of your loved one?[155]

Do your best to get enough sleep. Remember, it's not how long we live; it's how well we live. Sleep is vital to everyone's health and well being, especially someone in charge of caring for others. As I've stated, sleep deprived people have physical and mental impairments equal to people who are drunk.[156]

If your loved one is in the advanced stages of cognitive decline or affected by Alzheimer's, you may need to have someone stay over occasionally so you can get a good night's sleep. Don't feel guilty about this and don't hesitate to ask for help.

If you or your loved one can't sleep at night, get assistance from someone in your family or a paid helper. Don't feel guilty and don't hesitate to get help. Also consider re-arranging your loved one's room with an eye to safety considerations. Make certain the doors lock, for starters. Then if they wake up and begin pacing, they will be confined to their room and not bother you. Alzheimer's patients often exhibit anxiety and behavioral problems in the afternoon and evening, a condition commonly called sundowning.

DEALING WITH SUNDOWNING

Sundowners may become upset, angry, suspicious or disoriented in the late afternoon and evening. They may pace or wander. They sometimes hallucinate or become fixated on things that are not true.[157]

If you are struggling with the symptoms of sundowning, try some of the following:

- Create peaceful and serene afternoons and evenings

- Schedule appointments and trips for the morning

- Make certain that baths, showers, or other activities are accomplished in the morning or earlier in the day

- Modify the patient's diet—see Point 6 for excellent guidelines on this topic

- Anything with caffeine in it should not be given to your loved one in the afternoon. It's best to stop consumption of all caffeine, but if that is not possible, confine it to the morning.

- Serve dinner early

- Keep noise level to a minimum

- Restrict visitors in the evening

- Talk to your doctor, who may prescribe medication, or check for other problems, which might include depression or physical discomforts

- Consider an alternative to a bed. Some dementia patients sleep better in a chair or on a couch.

- Make certain your loved one gets exercise (you'll learn much more about this in Point 5). This can help tire them out and prevent pacing.[158]

PUT IT INTO ACTION: EXERCISES FOR POINT 4

1. Meditate and Take Time For Yourself.

Take what you've learned about meditation and "me" time such as writing in a journal and put it into action. An ideal time for "me" time is right before bed, as it forms a bridge between the business of the day and sleep.

2. Do a Sleep Check-up

Look at both the sleep environment and schedule. Following the guidelines listed in this chapter, check for variables in light, temperature and comfort level of the bed. Look into when the last food and drink is given to your loved one, and become aware of this for yourself. Minor adjustments in environment and schedule can make a big difference.

3. Devise a Consistent Sleep Plan

After you've taken care of the sleep environment and schedule, design a sleep ritual for yourself and your loved one. Think about making a cup of chamomile tea and spending a few minutes listening to music, or create your own sleep ritual. This has the same effect as meditating or writing in your journal before bed.

4. Sleep Between 11 PM and 7 AM

If at all possible, time your sleep to fall between these hours, as this is the time when the brain heals itself and memories form.

Point 5: Physical Exercise

Exercise is our next Point, and it is an exciting one. Now, when you think about exercise you might not get excited, particularly because finding time for it is difficult in your hectic schedule. But I get excited about exercise for many different reasons.

We all know that exercise has great physical benefits. I know how much better regular exercise makes me feel. You, too, may have experienced this first hand. Perhaps you've also noticed the stress-lowering effect of exercise, and the sense of well-being that it gives. Maybe you've used an exercise program to shed pounds and feel younger.

At the very least, you've read article after article that trumpets the value of exercise, right? Perhaps, though, this hasn't yet motivated you to get moving.

What if I told you that exercise is not only good for your body, but your mind, too? You see, the other reason I get so excited about exercise is that I know how good it is for the brain. I am familiar with emerging research which shows how exercise helps to prevent and even slow dementia.

If you're already participating in a regular exercise, program, bravo. Reading this chapter will reinforce your good habits and teach you about benefits you may not have known about.

If you have not yet started an exercise program, don't worry. We'll look at a variety of exercise programs and help you decide which will be best for you and your loved one. (Yes, exercise is necessary for people of any age and physical condition.) We'll also talk about setting goals and finding ways to get motivated. And of course, I'll give you suggestions for combining Points in order to make the best use of your time.

I feel strongly that once you read about the many beneficial results of exercise, you'll be eager to make the time for it. So let's get going. First let's look at all of the positive ways that exercise impacts the brain.

IMPACT OF EXERCISE ON THE BRAIN

Scientists are learning more and more about the workings of our brain, and their research is fascinating. Many studies are showing ways to lessen the chances of getting dementia and exercise is proving to figure prominently in prevention.

Exercise Creates Brand-New Brain Cells

Up until recently, it was thought that we were born with a finite number of brain cells. However, research has proven that humans constantly create new brain cells throughout the course of their lives. Princeton scientists reported in 1999 that there are several regions of the brain where new nerve cells, or neurons, develop.

This discovery has led to the promising field of *neurogenesis*, which is devoted to the birth of neurons. Neurogenesis shows us that the healthy brain is constantly creating. It renews itself with new thoughts, new experiences, new knowledge, and new ideas. Conversely, the brain is also affected by stressful conditions that can cause it to stagnate and waste away.[159]

From these studies, it is clear that mental stimulation plays a big role in creating healthy brain cells. We'll talk more about this in Point 8. But where does physical stimulation come into it? Researchers have recently discovered that aerobic exercise actually starts the process of birthing new brain neurons. Scientists at Columbia University found a way to measure the growth of nerve cells in the brains of regular exercisers. They discovered that exercising increased neurogenesis, or the creation of brain cells, particularly in a part of the brain which is linked with dementia.[160]

It's a Brain Builder

What happens when you exercise? Large amounts of blood moves swiftly throughout your body making sure all organs receive vital nutrients. Exercise also provides the brain with much needed oxygen that burns glucose, which is the fuel that gets your brain and memory to function optimally. While exercising, you speed up all of these processes. In fact, before you learn something new, you should exercise. Studies show that the heightened oxygen levels will help commit this information to memory much more efficiently. One way to help combine Points is to exercise (or simply stretch) before you begin your Brain Exercises and Art Rx that we'll get into in Point 8. The more you work out, the more fresh blood and oxygen is stimulating your brain as well as benefiting your circulation and memory making it a great brain builder.

Exercise Lowers the Risk for Alzheimer's and Dementia.

A University of Washington study found that older people who follow an exercise program at least 3 times a week are less likely to develop dementia or Alzheimer's. Scientists learned that these regular exercisers had a 30% to 40% lower risk of dementia. That is a significant reduction in risk for something as simple as getting out and moving your body a few times a week![161]

Exercise, of course, is also an effective tool against obesity. Why does this matter in preventing Alzheimer's? The simple fact is that the more overweight you are, the more likely you are to develop Alzheimer's or dementia.[162] You may have heard of the measurement called the Body Mass Index (BMI), which is commonly used to measure your body's ratio of fat to lean body mass. People with a BMI of 30 and above are more likely to develop dementia.[163]

A 2007 study found that, among the obese in general, the risks of dementia increased by 75%. However, among obese women, the risks of dementia increased by 200%.[164] Those are significant risk factors, and well worth considering as you plan your exercise program.

Isn't it amazing how something you might have thought was good for you physically also has so many benefits for your brain? Are you ready to commit to a regular exercise program yet? If you still aren't convinced that physical fitness is worth budgeting your time for, take a look at some of the other benefits.

Exercise Improves Quality of Life

In a recent study of postmenopausal women who were overweight, results showed that a small amount of daily exercise can have a positive impact on daily life. This was true with even as small an amount as 10 minutes a day. The study compared women who exercised for 6 months with women who did not exercise, and found that the women who exercised simply felt better. This was true across broad areas of physical and mental health, energy and in their interactions with others. You may not be postmenopausal, or even a female, but these results lend credence to the value of exercise for all kinds of people.[165]

Lowers Caregiver Stress

Remember how we talked about the benefits of relaxation and meditation? Caregivers are under an enormous amount of stress, and stress is insidious—you may not even realize that your insides are drenched in it. Caregiver stress can dramatically affect your health because bad choices such as poor eating habits and lack of exercise lead to obesity, high blood pressure, and high cholesterol, which in turn lead to heart attacks and stroke.[166] Exercise is vital to reducing stress. Your body can fight stress much more easily when it is in good condition.[167]

Good for Your Heart

Speaking of heart attacks, a healthy diet and regular exercise are the two keys to good cardiovascular health. Eating well simply isn't enough for optimum health. You need to exercise, too.[168]

Helps with Sundowning

Sundowning is late afternoon and evening agitation and energy in a person with dementia. Due to the sundowner's excess energy, one way to help cope with this issue is through physical exercise. Making sure your loved one gets a good walk or two in a day can help them tire and reduce the urge to pace or wander in the evening.[169]

Helps Get A Good Night's Sleep

I talked extensively about sleep in Point 4, but it is worth noting that exercise contributes to a restful night's sleep. Even moderate exercise can create better sleep. Just be certain not to exercise too late in the day, when it can make it difficult to fall asleep.[170]

It's never too late to start exercising

You can't get out of it by invoking the old cliché, too little, too late! No, exercise doesn't work that way. No matter what age you are and what your level of physical fitness, starting an exercise program will always be beneficial. In one study, scientists found seniors who exercised regularly lowered their risk of becoming disabled by 7% for each hour they were active. Not only that, regular activity also lowered mortality rates and helped seniors to participate in common daily activities.[171]

And so, the evidence is ample. The saying, "use it or lose it," refers not only to the brain but to the body as well. Shaking a leg will not only make you look and feel better, it will boost your brain power. Not only that, but it's a great Point-combining activity, since it helps to relax you (Point 2) and helps you to sleep (Point 4). And don't forget that exercising is also a great time to participate in Tunes Rx (Point 3). Plus, if you find an activity you enjoy, you'll also be utilizing Point 1. Exercise is a slam-dunk when it comes to Point combining, that's all there is to it!

EXERCISE PROGRAMS

Okay, I've convinced you. You're ready to begin an exercise program. Congratulations! If you've never exercised regularly before, you're going to love the way it makes you feel. If you already participate in an exercise program, read this section anyway. You might well learn some new tips and tricks to spice up your routine.

How Long?

Before we look at types of exercises, let's talk first about time, or more precisely, your lack of it. As a caregiver, one of your most precious commodities is time. You may well feel that there simply is never enough of it. Believe me, I understand.

I mention this now because not having enough time is a common excuse for not exercising. How can you take time to go to the gym or walk for an hour when you barely have time to cook dinner for your family? The good news is that you don't have to get your exercise in huge chunks.

Try to accomplish 30 minutes of exercise a day to begin. If finding 30 minutes in your day to exercise seems like a distant dream, don't despair. You don't have to do it all at once. You can break it up into 10 minutes segments, performed 3 times a day.

Perhaps you could take 10 minutes after lunch to walk—you'll feel more alert and livelier all afternoon if you do. Or get off the bus or subway one stop early in order to get in 10 minutes of walking. Do the same in the evening and you've almost gotten in your 30 minutes! Look for ways to add extra steps throughout the day, by parking farther away, or walking stairs instead of riding the elevator. Some people like to wear pedometers to count how many steps they have taken in a day.

The trick with exercise is to do it regularly enough so that you see and feel the benefits. Once you experience that, it becomes a self-fulfilling process. Because you know how good it makes you feel, you'll be eager to propel yourself out the door for whatever form of exercise you have chosen.

Remember, it is okay to start slow and easy and for a few minutes at a time. Before you know it, you'll be finding all kinds of ways to add exercise into your daily routine.

What Kind of Exercise?

First a word of caution. You may want to consult your physician before you start an exercise program. If you have been physically inactive for a long time, are a man over 40, or a woman over 50, it is especially important that you do so, and it is recommended by the Surgeon General.

One thing to consider with exercise is to not allow yourself to get bored. Boredom is a sure route to quitting exercise. Besides, we're looking for ways to add quality to your life, not create more drudgery. If you tend to tire of doing the same thing over and over again, vary your exercise program. We'll be looking at the following types of exercises in this chapter:

- Endurance

- Strength Training

- Stretching

- Balance

The best approach to take with exercise is to get some of each type, as they are all important, according to the National Institute on Aging at the National Institute of Health.[172] You may naturally find yourself drawn to one type over another, and that is fine, but also work on getting some of the other kinds into your routine. If you like to walk, for instance, you can do simple stretching and balancing exercises before heading out the door. Or, incorporate some basic stretches into your strength training routine.

Remember also that all types of exercises can be done alone at home or at the gym, in a group with regular classes. You may want to look into joining a gym, or enlisting a friend to walk with you. If your loved one lives in a group facility, check into the possibility of exercise classes there. Many senior centers encourage exercise by holding classes.

Now let's look at each kind of exercise separately:

Endurance

Endurance exercises pump up your heart rate and your breathing for an extended period of time. Activities such as walking, jogging, swimming, bicycling or hiking are all endurance exercises. These exercises benefit the health of the heart and circulatory systems, and as we have just seen, also assist the brain. If you've not done any endurance exercises in awhile, start slow. You can begin with as little as 5 minutes a day.[173]

Bear in mind that aerobic exercise forces you to move the muscles in your legs and buttocks. In turn, this causes your heart and lungs to work harder, which is good for them because you'll be pumping oxygen to every part of your body. We've already learned that increasing the flow of oxygen to the brain is extremely beneficial. Aerobic activities can include exercise classes, dancing, walking, hiking, jogging, running, bicycling or swimming.[174]

Strength Training

These exercises build muscle tissue and at the same time prevent and reduce muscle loss. They have the added benefit of increasing your metabolism. This will help you to lose weight and balance your blood sugars.[175]

You may feel that you are too old, or that the person you are caring for is too old to bother to begin strength training. But nothing could be further from the truth. The body deteriorates as we age, and part of that deterioration is in our muscles and bones. An outgrowth of this is a lessening in our strength. Why should you worry about declining muscles? After all, you probably have no desire to look like a Mr. or Mrs. Universe—and your loved one most certainly does not! However, you must keep strength training because falls can result from low bone density and muscle tone. When older people fall they are prone to injuries that can be life-threatening or debilitating.

You also may not realize that muscle loss goes beyond consequences to your physical strength. We've seen how exercise increases the flow of oxygen to the entire body. But well- developed muscles use this oxygen and distribute the nutrients we need more efficiently. Believe it or not, strong muscles also play a role in helping cells remove sugar from the blood and maintain correct levels of insulin. Thus, weight training is also beneficial because developed muscles play a huge role in the avoidance of type-2 Diabetes and obesity.

Ill-developed muscles can simply make day to day life more complex. It's harder to participate in even the simplest of activities and can adversely affect balance (increasing the chance of a fall).[176] For all these reasons, strength training is vital for you, the caregiver, to begin now. And there's no time like the present to begin a simple strength training routine with your senior loved one. It should come as no surprise that for all these reasons weight training for seniors is the recommendation of more and more scientists and doctors.[177]

So what are weight training exercises? You're probably most familiar with lifting free weights and this is a good option for seniors because they can start with very light weights, even using a book or a soup can. Other options are using weight machines at a gym or exercise room in a senior center, calisthenics, or using the stretchy, resistance bands.

Stretching

Stretching exercises help keep you limber and flexible. Used in combination with endurance activities, they can help prevent injury from exercise. Stretching not only makes you feel good, but it has many other benefits as well. These include improving your posture and good old fashioned relaxation (good for a little Point combining!) Remember, though, that they do not affect endurance or strength on their own.

You can do simple stretching exercises on our own or with your senior, or participate in a class such as yoga or Tai Chi. Whichever option you choose, consider the following guidelines to keep your stretching safe and easy:

- Do a mini-warm-up for your muscles first. March in place, swing your arms, or swing your hips from side to side.

- Stretch gently and slowly. Stretching is not meant to be rushed through! Also remember to exhale as you stretch. Breathe out for as long as possible.

- Hold each pose for 10 to 30 seconds and remember not to pulse, but stay in position.

- If you are designing a home-stretching routine, be certain to include all the major muscle groups. You might want to start with your leg muscles, stretching the calves, hamstrings and quadriceps. Then move up to the hips and buttocks. Stretch your stomach and chest muscles, then your shoulder and arm muscles, and don't forget your neck! Ahhhh. After tensing, relaxing and stretching out your muscles, you'll be purring like a cat.[178]

Balance

Falling is a big issue among seniors, and balance exercises can maintain adult independence by preventing falls. We'll look further into balance and the issue of falls in depth later in this chapter. Balance exercises also build leg muscles.[179]

Why Not Try Tai Chi?

Have you ever passed a park where a group of people are doing Tai Chi? Or looked into the window of a martial arts studio when a Tai Chi group is in session? If so, you know that watching this ancient discipline is very compelling. Not only is Tai Chi relaxing to perform, it is also very relaxing to watch. Tai Chi improves balance, which we've learned is vital for the elderly, and it also improves coordination and lowers stress, which is good for everyone. Tai Chi is my kind of exercise, seeing as how it combines many of my Points!

When I say Tai Chi is ancient, I mean it is ancient, having been prominent in China for 2,000 years. Tai Chi combines physical exercise, meditation and martial arts, consisting of a series of gentle, easy movements. It's amazing, but these slow movements are designed to calm your mind and work to restore a general level of overall health. Unlike the Western style of calisthenics you might be used to, Tai Chi is not a series of exercises with brief breaks in between. Rather, Tai Chi movements all flow together, with each of a possible 100 poses flowing one after the other without pause.

Because there are so many possible positions, Tai Chi is very adaptable. You can stick with the movements you know and feel comfortable with, or you can constantly experiment. Tai Chi is low-impact and low-intensity. It is appropriate for people at a variety of ability levels. Some of it is faster paced, but there are plenty of slower styles that your loved one might enjoy. Tai Chi has been proven to improve balance and coordination, increase stamina, reduce blood pressure, promote relaxation and improve your mood. That's a lot of benefit wrapped up in one simple exercise method!

Tai Chi is easy to learn, and once you've learned the movements you can practice them every day on your own, or with others. You can learn from a book, website, or DVD. But why not do a little Point combining and seek out a class?

Many locations offer Tai Chi. Look for classes at senior centers, community colleges, martial arts studios, or neighborhood centers.[180]

Overall Notes on Exercise

This rundown of the various types of exercise needed for healthy living should give you a good start at creating your own physical fitness program. Hopefully, it gives you some good ideas on how to get your senior loved one active, too. Remember to always check with your doctor before beginning an exercise program.

Beginning an exercise program can be as simple as lacing up your sneakers and walking out the front door. But you may prefer to join an aerobics class, or find a gym that offers circuit training—which combines strength training and endurance. The key is to find a program that you will enjoy and stick with.

MOTIVATION

Ah, motivation, that all-important key to starting—and maintaining—any good habit. If we were all consistently motivated, we'd all eat right and exercise constantly. All you have to do is take a look around the nearest shopping mall to know that many of us lack motivation. At any mall, grocery store, or group event in America, you'll see numerous obese people, many of them plunked down on a bench, too tired to walk or participate in physical activities. Clearly, motivation is an important issue.

It may be even more difficult for the busy caregiver to get motivated to exercise. It is so much easier to stop at the fast food joint on the way home from the care center and afterwards plop yourself in front of the television with a pint of ice cream. You may have started the day with good intentions to come home and exercise, but somewhere along the way those good intentions got derailed.

90

So let's take a look at motivation and how you can make it work for you to create an exercise plan.

Different people enjoy different activities and have varying responses to ideas. What motivates your best friend may not motivate you at all. What motivates your best friend's daughter may leave her cold. And so forth. Take a look at the following factors that have been proven to motivate people:

- **Your Appearance.** Let's face it—some of us are just plain vain! Despite the fact that the bible says, "All is vanity,"[181] sometimes vanity can be a good thing. When we have put on a few pounds or started to sag in various places, it makes us uncomfortable. You might notice that your clothes don't fit as well and then you feel you have nothing to wear. Appearance can be a powerful motivator!

- **Social Opportunities.** This works in two ways. First of all, if you are unhappy with your appearance, you may decline social invitations. This can eventually lead to loneliness and depression. Second, exercising with family (perhaps your senior loved one?) or friends can give you a chance to visit. In the busy day of a caregiver, this may be the only time you have to spend with friends. Arranging to meet a friend to take a walk makes it much harder to decline to exercise—you'll be letting down yourself *and* someone else.

- **Enjoyment.** It just feels good to move and stretch and safely exert your body. It may be difficult to believe as you struggle to begin an exercise program, but soon the pure pleasure of feeling your body move may be enough motivation to get you going.[182]

Do any of those motivate you? Use them! The next time you are tempted to forgo the strength training routine, visualize the pair of jeans you can no longer fit into. Remember how tight they were across the stomach? That ought to get you going. Or think about the dress you want to wear to your niece's graduation.

Ponder if you know anybody who would like to begin an exercise program with you. Meeting your husband at the gym after a long and trying afternoon could be a bright spot in your day.

Another way to harness the power of motivation is to plan rewards for yourself.[183] (Just don't fall into the trap of using unhealthy rewards, such as fattening foods or caloric liquor!) Rewarding yourself is especially beneficial for the overwhelmed caregiver, because it combines several Points at once. There's having fun (Point 1), relaxation, (Point 2) and exercise (Point 5, this Point). Rewarding yourself for exercising regularly is a great treat for the caregiver.

Go back to the Joy List you made at the beginning of this book. Maybe you'd like to spend an afternoon reading a book. Or perhaps your idea of a heavenly afternoon is to visit a museum, or gallery hop. Meet a friend for a movie, or a morning of shopping. Follow the shopping trip with a relaxing pedicure or spa. Better yet, plan a whole spa day.[184] Choose several items from it to use as your rewards. Then put on your walking shoes and head out the door!

Goal Setting

Okay, I'll admit it—goal setting is not the sexiest of topics. You're probably rolling your eyes at the thought of it already. But now that you are a caregiver, you are in a different situation than you've ever been before. New situations call for new actions. Remember, you have the choice to make the most of your situation or make it into a living hell. Mastering the art of goal setting can help you make your life more pleasant.

SMART Goals

You probably have heard that it is important to write down your goals. But perhaps when you have tried to do this, you've been perplexed by how, exactly to state them. Maybe your goals seemed vague and unclear. There's an easy way to solve that problem. Always remember to create SMART goals. What is a SMART goal? Many time-management and productivity experts recommend the use of SMART goals. You may have even seen them mentioned in various places, but not been certain what, exactly they are. SMART goals are an amazing tool that you can use to make certain your goals are as effective as they can be. The CDC defines SMART goals as:

S = Specific
M = Measurable
A = Attainable
R = Relevant
T = Time-based

Here's an example. Your specific long-term goal may be to attain a higher level of fitness while the short-term goal may be to start walking. It is measurable because you can ask yourself if you've begun (it's difficult to deny if you haven't). It is attainable because you know you are capable of walking, at least around the block! Set a specific time limit such as you'll begin within one week and walk for 30 minutes to make it time-based. And you know that it is relevant because beginning a walking program fits in with your overall goal of attaining a higher fitness level.[185] Using the SMART goal system is an easy way to design goals that will actually work for you.

Short and Long-Term Goals

If you were planning to drive from Los Angeles to New York, what is the first thing you would do? I don't know about you, but the first thing I would do is consult a good map. I'd want to have a visual image of where I was going, and plan rest stops and overnight trips along the way. Setting goals is much like following a road map, with your ultimate goal being the final destination on the map.

Say, for instance, that your ultimate goal is "get fit and lose 25 pounds." As you begin your exercise program, shedding those 25 pounds can look as distant as Manhattan does on the map. You wouldn't attempt to drive all the way to New York City without a few stops along the way. Nor should you attempt to reach your long-term goal without setting short-term goals as markers for your progress.

Because you now know the process of creating and setting SMART goals, you'll be able to design attainable short and long-term goals. One of the keys to achieving long-term goals is to break them up into manageable steps. Break your long-term SMART goals into short-term SMART goals.

To return to the above example, let's assume your goal is to begin a walking program. Here are some of the short-term goals you may break "starting" into:

- Talk to my doctor about beginning.

- Check on the condition of my walking shoes; buy new ones if needed.

- Dig out exercise clothing or buy new if needed.

- Schedule 3 30-minute walking sessions.

- Ask my best friend to join me!

See how creating SMART short-term goals to support your overall goal of starting to walk makes it easy to see exactly what you need to do?

VISUALIZE YOUR GOALS

Remember the visualization breathing exercise in Point 2? We used the technique of visualizing to relax and transform you into a positive mindset. You can also use visualization to build confidence by envisioning yourself participating in exercise or other goals. You'll find a step by step visualization listed in the exercises at the end of this chapter, which can be used during your "me" time or at any time during the day when you want to reinforce a goal. All you have to do is envision yourself on the golf course, or hiking a mountain trail. Visualize yourself skiing with grace and ease, or running around a track.[186] Some people believe that visualizing physical movement has almost the same effect as actually doing it, so you'll be giving yourself a double dose of goodness.

FALLING

Now that you have gotten your exercise program well under way, it is time to turn our attention back to the loved one you are caring for. One of the benefits of exercise for seniors and those suffering from dementia is that it can help with the issues surrounding falling.

Unless you have personal experience with a loved one falling, you may not realize what a common and debilitating problem falls are for seniors. But here's a startling statistic: after the age of 65, one in three people experience a fall every year. Making falls the leading cause of nonfatal injuries, hospital admissions and injury deaths for older adults.[187]

The statistics tell the tale—falls are a very real danger for our seniors. Falls can result in injury, either minor, or major, such as hip fractures. Falls can also cause a fear of falling again. Falls can also be the beginning of other health problems. One statistic states that one in five seniors die within a year after they've broken a hip.[188]

Causes of Falls

While it would be easy to assume that most falls are simply the result of getting older and frailer, this is not always the case. There are a number of other factors that can contribute to falls as well. Medication or a combination of medications with side effects like dizziness and light-headedness can be one such cause. There are many diseases and physical problems such as stroke, Parkinson's disease, poor vision and dementia that can contribute. There are also factors within the home, such as rugs, and dimly lit areas that can create hazards. Remember too, often times falling, or simply the fear of falling, can be the result of a mixture of all these physical, environmental, and emotional causes.[189]

Fall Risks

The best way to deal with falls is to prevent them. But how will you know if your loved one is at risk for falling? Consult the list below and answer each question for your loved one honestly. If six or more of the descriptions fit your loved one, you need to make an appointment for them to see the doctor.

- Over 60 Years Old
- Hospitalized in the Last Year
- Uses a Cane or Walker
- Sometimes Loses Balance
- Feels Weakness in Their Body
- Is Sometimes Disoriented
- Has Fallen in Last 3 Months
- Is Forgetful
- Is Impulsive
- Feels Sense of Urgency to Eliminate
- Requires Assistance to Eliminate
- Is Incontinent
- Is Taking Laxatives or Diuretics
- Is Taking Four or More Medications

- Is Taking Medications That May Impair Thought Processes, Cause Vertigo, Lower Blood Pressure, or Cause Central Nervous System Changes

Again, if six or more of these descriptions fit your loved one, please discuss the issue of falling with the doctor.[190]

Fear of Falling

Did you know that the fear of falling is a significant concern among seniors? It is, and it can affect their mobility at home and anywhere else in the world. Fear of falling can be almost as debilitating as the fall itself. Often the elderly who become the most fearful are those who have had close friends or family members experience a fall. If fear of falling becomes overwhelming, it can lead to your loved one becoming less active. Then the vicious cycle begins—decreased movement leads to increased fragility and that, in turn can cause a fall.[191]

Fear of falling can have a long-term and debilitating impact on seniors. These fears can lead to loneliness and seclusion due to self-limited activities, and can ultimately lead to depression.[192]

Preventing Falling

Here are the six main guidelines, as recommended by the Mayo Clinic, to prevent falling:

1. See Your Physician
2. Keep Moving
3. Wear Sensible Shoes
4. Remove Home Hazards
5. Light Up Your Living Space
6. Use Assistive Devices[193]

A couple of these are self-evident, such as seeing the doctor and wearing sensible shoes, but others require a bit more thought. Now I want to talk about movement (after all, this is a chapter on exercise) and specifically, balance.

Balance

One of the most important tools to avoiding a fall is good balance. Those of us who are relatively healthy and sturdy don't think about it much, but even the simplest of daily activities requires good balance. In order to walk, attend mealtime, go shopping, or visit with others, it is important for your loved one to be stable on their feet.

The senior who fears falling and doesn't get out as much, runs a terrible risk of having their nerve connections that control balance deteriorate. This is why the fear of falling can have such a negative effect. It's a vicious cycle!

Our bodies and brains work together in amazing, subtle ways that we take for granted—until a fall or some other crisis occurs. So let's look at ways to keep the bodies and brains of our seniors stable and balanced.

The key to restoring balance is exercise. Balance exercises can be fun and easy, and you can make them a part of your regular caregiving visit. This combines Point 1(Fun) with Point 5 (Exercise). While you're at it, put on some music and make the exercise lively. You'll be getting a good dose of Tunes Rx (Point 3) at the same time. Strive to get your loved one to participate in the exercises daily.

Exercises for Fall Prevention

Exercise to prevent falling should focus on the following areas:

- Balance, of course

- Strengthening of the core and abdomen

- Improving awareness of your surroundings and alertness

- Improving sensitivity to tactile elements

- Working to build hip and leg strength

- Increasing confidence in basic movement[194]

Please refer to the exercise section at the end of this chapter for complete, simple exercises to use in fall prevention.

PUT IT INTO ACTION: EXERCISES FOR POINT 5

1. Set SMART Exercise Goals

Give yourself 10 minutes to half an hour to set your goals. You can do this as part of your "me" time or spend a little extra time on it during the day—at lunch, for instance, or on your coffee break. Review the section on SMART goals and set a long-term goal for yourself (i.e., lose 20 pounds.) Now break that into short-term, easily attainable goals.

A good way to do this is to ask yourself, am I ready to start now? So, for instance if your long-term goal is to lose 20 pounds and you want to start exercising at a gym, ask yourself, am I ready to start? In other words, can you walk out the door, get in the car and go to the gym right now? If not, why not? You might need to buy a gym membership, which will require researching which gym is the best for your needs. You may need to buy shoes and clothing and a water bottle. Asking yourself, am I ready to start now? Gives you a way to break what can be a big, overwhelming long-term goal into small, easy to accomplish pieces.

2. Use Deep Breathing and Visualization

Go back and choose any of the deep breathing exercises in Point 2. Get yourself into a calm relaxed state and imagine yourself participating in your chosen activity. See it, smell it, feel it, hear it, experience it.

If you want to hike in the woods regularly, for instance, imagine yourself at the trail head, strapping a backpack on your back and checking for water. What does the area look like? Can you smell spring flowers or nearby water? What sounds do you hear? How does it feel to take a deep breath and set off? Now imagine yourself striding along the trail, confidently and strongly. Focus on that image for a few moments.

You can adapt this visualization for any exercise you want to participate in, be it golf, or strength training, or swimming. Get your mind going in the direction you want your body to go.

3. Plan Celebrations

Return to the Joy List you created in Point 1. Look over it again—add some more to it if you like! Now choose some celebrations or rewards you can give yourself when you've completed certain short-term goals.

If you need to find a gym to join, for instance, you might want to give yourself a shopping trip to buy gym clothes after you have researched and found one to join. Choose rewards that will make you happy, not what you think you should choose because someone else likes them.[195]

4. Pick Balance Exercises for Your Loved One (and don't forget yourself!)

It may seem daunting to have to add exercises into the list of things you must do with your loved one, but it doesn't have to be. You only have to do the exercises once a day and starting out nice and easy is the recommendation. Start by practicing the first exercise on the list with your senior. When they have mastered it, move on to the next. Remember, once a day is your best bet to gain results and increase health. If you can't be with them once a day, ask for help from a family member (or a nurse).

Here are a couple of exercises that are recommended by the AARP and that I use with my patients:

Walk the Line – Have them imagine they are on a tight-rope and walk heel to toe straight forward for 10-20 steps and then have them walk backwards the same distance toe to heel.

Leg Balances - Have your senior stand on one leg for 30 seconds. He will probably want to hold onto a table or chair for stability, at least at first. Repeat with the other leg for 30 seconds.

Sit and Stand – Have them sit in a chair and then stand up. Repeat.[196] For more of a challenge (maybe this would be better for you) do this while standing on one leg and then switch to the other.

Core Strengthening Exercises

This exercise uses an inflatable exercise ball, widely available at sporting-goods stores.

- Place the ball near to a counter or table, and sit on it with feet flat on the floor. Your senior may need to spend some time first just getting used to the feeling of being on the ball. When she is ready, have her rock side to side, and then forward and back. Remember, these are gentle motions. Nothing too rowdy, please! Do this exercise for 1 minute at first, and work up to 10.

- Is the above exercise getting too tame for your loved one? Here's an advanced variation. Follow the same rocking motions, as above but this time, do it while lifting one foot off the floor.[197]

Hip and Leg Strength Exercises

- Seated March - Have your senior sit in a chair. As with all of these exercises, you may want to do this right along with him. Lift one knee as high as possible and hold for a count of 3. Lower and repeat with the other leg. Gradually work up to where you are doing 10 lifts for each leg. This is similar to marching in place while sitting down.

- Knee Lift - Stand next to something stable to hold onto. Bend your knee and then lift it as high as you can. Hold for a count of 10. Repeat 10 consecutive times with each leg. This exercise is like an exaggerated marching in place.

Face Your Fears Exercise

- Begin by putting your hands on a wall at shoulder level. Your arms should be nearly straight. Lean toward the wall to feign falling and practice breaking the fall by stepping forward. When your senior does this exercise, you will want to supervise her carefully. It can be a bit intimidating, though it is very good for increasing confidence.

- The advanced move is to stand a little farther away from the wall. Catch yourself by putting hands on the wall if necessary.[198]

Heightened Sensitivity Exercise

- Forget what your mother used to tell you—its good to go barefoot. Now turnabout is fair play as you convince her to walk barefoot. (This adds a bit of Point 1, fun, to the exercise.) Going barefoot is an excellent way to increase sensitivity through differences in tactile mediums. Encourage your loved one to go barefoot at home and ask him to feel the difference between the rug and the hardwood floor and the tile of the bathroom. Go barefoot on the lawn or on the beach. Choose surfaces that are safe, yet slightly uneven. You may need to give your senior an arm to lean on for this exercise. [199]

5. Remove Home Hazards

Be mindful of obvious home hazards, it could mean the difference between them being able to stay in their beloved house or move to a senior facility.

Point 6: Brain Tune Up® Eating Plan

Oh, that awful word—diet. You may cringe as you even read it. You may have been on numerous diets throughout your life, with varying degrees of success. Most people equate diets with deprivation, hunger, and longing.

If that's how you feel about diets, take heart, because I have excellent news for you. So-called diets don't have to be difficult to follow, with tiny portions of bland foods. Eating the Brain Tune Up way gives you lots of choices for delicious, and nutritious foods that will make you feel great. Not only that, but my eating plan is good for your body *and* your brain. By eating the Brain Tune Up way, you'll be taking optimal care of every part of your wonderful self.

Furthermore, my Brain Tune Up eating plan is good for you *and* your loved one. No cooking separate meals or having to remember who should be eating what. Everyone can—and should—be eating the same thing.

Remember that it is always an excellent idea to check with your doctor, or your loved one's doctor, before making any major changes in the way you eat.

HIGHLIGHTS OF THE BRAIN TUNE UP® EATING PLAN

I'd like to start by introducing you to the basics of the Brain Tune Up eating plan before I tell you in detail why it is so good for you. The Brain Tune Up eating plan is based on the Mediterranean diet. You've probably heard the term Mediterranean diet bandied about and you might have assumed it was yet another diet fad. However, nothing could be further from the truth.

The Mediterranean diet is based on the eating patterns of the 16 countries that border the Mediterranean Sea. As you might imagine, among these countries, and even within specific regions of each Mediterranean country, there is a great deal of difference in patterns of food consumption. It just stands to reason that differences in society, religion, economy and agriculture would create different diets.[200] Think about the great variety of food within the various regions of the United States. Southern cooking differs from foods you might find up north, for instance. But there is also a great deal of similarity in the diets of Americans (and not all for the good, unfortunately). Such is also the case with the Mediterranean countries, and nutritionists have isolated the following similarities:

- Olive oil is the most used fat source. As a mono-unsaturated fat, it has certain health benefits we'll learn more about later.

- The food categories consumed consists of fruits, vegetables, bread and cereals, potatoes, beans, nuts, grains, and seeds.

- Dairy products, fish and poultry are eaten in low to moderate amounts. Red meat is rarely eaten.

- Eggs are eaten up to four times a week.

- Wine is enjoyed in moderate amounts.[201]

These are the basics of a healthy eating plan: Lots of fruits, vegetables, fish and whole grains with little or no saturated and trans fats. This plan looks pretty straightforward, right? So why am I so excited about such a simple plan? Because this simple and delicious way of eating has big benefits for the brain. Let's take a look at what gets me so excited.

BENEFITS OF THE BRAIN TUNE UP® EATING PLAN

The Mediterranean diet has long been recognized as being heart healthy. Following such a diet, particularly when combined with other healthy habits such as losing extra weight, practicing regular relaxation techniques, and exercising consistently has many other benefits as well. (Sounds a lot like what we've been talking about, right?) After a few months on the Mediterranean diet, you may notice that your blood pressure and your cholesterol levels have been lowered. And such a diet can also help to keep blood sugar and insulin at healthy levels. We now also know that the Mediterranean diet is good for your brain, too.[202]

Following the Brain Tune Up eating plan will have a huge beneficial effect on you—it'll help your brain, your heart, and your overall level of health tremendously. I'd like to share with you a bit more about how this diet can benefit your brain in particular.

Lowers the Risk of Alzheimer's Disease

According to a 2006 study from Columbia University Medical Center, a Mediterranean-style diet can lower the risk of Alzheimer's disease by as much as 68%.[203] This is good news not only on a personal level, but on a societal one. As the baby boomer generation enters their retirement years, Alzheimer's is poised to become a huge public health issue.

Why is this? One look at the statistics tells the tale. An estimated 14 million baby boomers will develop some form of dementia, including Alzheimer's.[204] This is so dire because 2008 marks the first year baby boomers begin to collect social security.

Because these figures are so staggering, researching and discovering ways to prevent Alzheimer's disease is very important. More and more studies point to the role of diet.

An ongoing study at Columbia University Medical Center followed 2,258 elderly men who ate the Mediterranean diet and found that the men who most closely followed the diet had the lowest risk of Alzheimer's. This study was the first to look at specific diet habits, the way that people eat foods in combination, rather than focusing on one certain food.[205]

A 2002 Finnish study of 1,500 people determined that people with high cholesterol and high blood pressure had the highest risk of developing Alzheimer's disease. And of course we already know that the Mediterranean diet is a heart healthy diet.[206]

A Harvard University study found that women who ate green leafy vegetables and cruciferous vegetables such as broccoli had a smaller decline in cognitive skills.[207]

Finally, research at the Medical University of South Carolina showed that mice consuming a diet heavy in saturated fat and cholesterol performed poorly on memory tasks. They also exhibited high levels of the toxic brain protein beta amyloid, which is linked to Alzheimer's.[208]

Prolongs the Life of Alzheimer's Patients

Other research has focused on the links between diet and patients who already have Alzheimer's. A study noted in the medical journal *Neurology* showed that the Mediterranean diet appeared to lower the death rate among Alzheimer's patients. The patients in this study who most closely followed the Mediterranean diet lived longer than those who ate a typical Western one. (This study showed a mortality risk reduction of 73%, with the average survival rate of those on the Mediterranean diet of four years longer than those not on it.[209]

Reduces Caregiver Stress

We've already talked extensively about the importance of relaxation (Point 2) as an antidote to your stressful life as a caregiver. Diet also plays a role in stress. The choices you make for food and drink will also affect your stress level. When you are busy and rushed, it is easy to visit the drive-through at the fast food restaurant, or rely on sugar and caffeine to get you through the day. These diet choices offer only temporary pick-me-ups, however. Choosing healthy foods like fruits, vegetables, fish and whole grains will give you long lasting energy levels.

Here are specific dietary guidelines to ease stress:

- **Watch Caffeine**. A little goes a long way. Bear in mind that caffeine is not all bad, so if you can't exist without your morning cup of Java, take heart. Small amounts of caffeine can have a positive impact on concentration and performance. But large amounts, over a couple of cups a day can not only increase your jitters, anxiety and stress, it can also cause insomnia.

- **Drink Alcohol in Moderation**. Alcohol can have a calming effect in small amounts, and it is known to be good for the heart. Too much, however, increases your risk for other diseases. Plus you run the risk of addiction.

- **Reduce Sodium**. Overdoing the salt intake may cause you to retain fluids. This is because sodium tends to stress your system, including your metabolism. Consume highly processed foods laden with salt sparingly.

- **Lower Sugar Consumption**. Most of us are well aware that sugar can cause weight gain and wreak havoc with your insulin and blood sugar levels. But did you know that sugar also stresses your pancreas? Yet one more reason to lessen the amount of sugar you eat or stay away from it entirely.

Those are the items on the "watch" list. Now let's look at all the wonderful things that will help your body deal with stress.

- **Meat and Fish.** When I say meat, I mean lean meat. Don't make the mistake of relying solely on red meat for your protein choices. You're probably aware that red meat is high in cholesterol and saturated fat, and also that these are not good for you. But did you know that they can cause added stress on your body? On the other hand, lean meat, fish and poultry are good choices for protein. They are also full of B vitamins and zinc. Fish such as mackerel, sardines and salmon are high in omega-3 fatty acids.

- **Fruits**. Ah, nature's bounty shines in fruit. Berries such as strawberries and blueberries, and other fruits, such as mango, kiwi and pineapple are not only naturally sweet and tasty, they are also bursting with vitamins, minerals and antioxidants.

- **Starchy Vegetables**. For once, something starchy is good for you! Root vegetables such as winter squash, sweet potatoes, and turnips have high levels of beta carotene and folate.

- **Milk**. While the Mediterranean diet does not rely heavily on dairy products, a couple of servings a day can help you manage your weight. Milk is also full of calcium and B vitamins.[210]

By adhering to my Brain Tune Up eating plan, you'll be benefiting your stress levels, your physical health, and the condition of your brain. I'll go into more detail about the eating plan, but first I want to mention one more benefit.

Lessens Sundowning

As we have learned, sundowning is late afternoon confusion and agitation in a dementia sufferer. One promising way to cope with sundowning is with diet. Obviously, restricting their caffeine intake is necessary. Many professional caregivers have found positive results with moving dinnertime to an earlier hour. You have to experiment with this to see what time works best for your loved one. And as we have already learned in this chapter, a diet high in vegetables, fruits and lean proteins will be the most beneficial for your loved one, no matter what their condition.

A WORD ABOUT ANTIOXIDANTS

Many foods that researchers now recommend are those that are high in antioxidant content. Why am I so bullish on antioxidants? More and more research is confirming that antioxidants pack a disease-fighting wallop. They can fight cancer, prevent heart disease, slow aging, and yes, ward off dementia.[211]

Where do you find these wonder substances? You guessed it—they are abundant in vegetables, fruits, nuts, whole grains, legumes, poultry, fish and meat—in other words, all the basic elements of the Brain Tune Up eating plan. New antioxidants are constantly being discovered and consequently, we're learning more about these important substances all the time. As an example, just one class of antioxidant, the flavonoids, number more than 4,000![212]

Free Radicals

Here's a basic primer on antioxidants that will help you understand why these substances are so important. We all understand that our very existence depends on oxygen, which breathes life into our bodies. What you may not know is that one main function of oxygen is to burn food into energy. That's the good part of oxygen, and without it we wouldn't be able to exist. But oxygen is also a troublemaker. Oxygen and the oxidation process damages tissues. Oxygen is missing an electron and it grabs whatever it can. A free radical is an oxygen molecule that is missing an electron.

Free radicals are aptly named, because just like political radicals, they will attack whatever cells are nearby them. This includes protein, fats, and DNA. After a free radical attack, these poor molecules are mere shadows of their former selves. Too many free radicals in the body have been tied to many diseases such as heart disease and cancer. Enter antioxidants, which glory in neutralizing free radicals by donating electrons. It is like calling in the cavalry to quell the rebels.[213]

Antioxidants are broken down into two groups:

- Vitamins and minerals with antioxidant abilities

- Organic compounds found in plant foods

Antioxidants have numerous benefits besides their electron rebuilding capabilities. One very important benefit is minimizing inflammation, which underlies many diseases. Our friends the antioxidants also work hard to keep our arteries open and take care of our DNA. Each class of antioxidant has specific benefits.

We know that antioxidants like to work together, not alone, so eating a variety of antioxidant rich foods will be the most beneficial. Antioxidants are not stored in the body, so it's not enough to eat junk food all week and devote one day to healthy eating.[214]

Because they are not stored during the day, it is important to consume antioxidant-rich foods throughout the day. The best source of antioxidants is fruits and vegetables and whole grains. [215] By following the Brain Tune Up eating plan, you'll assure yourself of ingesting enough antioxidants to wage a full-fledged war against the free radicals.

HELPFUL BRAIN TUNE UP® EATING PLAN TIPS

Now that you've had a crash course in healthy food choices, all you have to do is go forth and make them. I know, I know—easier said than done. To help ease your transition to the Brain Tune Up eating plan, I've gathered some tips that are listed below. Remember, it isn't a diet, it's a lifestyle. You'll be making permanent changes in your eating habits, and changing habits is hard. Give yourself credit for every new healthy habit you start!

- Good old fashioned home cooking is still the best, because you can limit the fat and sodium that you cook with. Confine eating out, whether at a fast-food or regular restaurant, to once a week.

- Along the same lines, allow yourself a small treat once a week. This is especially helpful if you've been craving a sweet dessert.

- Cut saturated fat. Choose olive oil to cook with, and look for light versions of butter, cheese, ice cream, and other dairy products.

- Remove skin from chicken.

- Eat egg whites or egg substitute.

- Avoid high-fat meats like hot dogs and sausage.

- Choose whole grains like barley, brown rice, bulgur, buckwheat, kasha, stone-ground corn-meal, whole wheat couscous, quinoa, rolled oats and polenta.

- Eat fatty fish! This includes salmon, sardines, mackerel, tuna and lake trout.

- Limit sodium to one teaspoon daily or half that if you have high blood pressure. Use herbs, lemon juice, or vinegars to enhance flavors.

- Serve red meat no more than once a week. Instead eat fish, poultry, or plant foods. Aim for 2 to 3 meals of poultry per week and 2 meatless dinners per week. Experiment with meatless dinners such as meat-free chili, stir-fried veggies with tofu or peanuts, and so forth.

- Limit snacks to less than 200 calories. If you're not careful, the calories from snacks can really add up. Try vegetables with low-fat dip, apples or celery with natural peanut butter, popcorn, cottage cheese, or fruit.

- Exercise! But you're already doing that, because you've read Point 5, right?

- Be wary of alcohol consumption. Red wine in moderation is good for you, but too much of it is not. Moderate for women means one drink a day while men can get away with two.

- Most important of all, enjoy! We live amidst amazing abundance with a wide variety of foods that are good for us. Revel in the choices that you have.[216]

One last tip about breakfast

Believe it or not, there are real benefits to the brain from eating breakfast. Consuming a healthy meal in the morning has been proven to improve mental performance overall. Studies of children through the years have consistently shown that those who eat breakfast perform better in school.

Why such dramatic results? After an entire night without food, both your body and your brain need to be restocked with nutrients. Research has shown the benefits of eating breakfast to your body, also. One of the biggest is that breakfast eaters lose weight more successfully than non-breakfast eaters.

What should you eat for breakfast? It does make a difference. Avoid the highly processed and sugary cereals and breakfast bars that many reach for. Instead, opt for a high-fiber carbohydrate and a lean protein. This combination will keep you going because it is absorbed slowly by the body, giving you a consistent energy level all morning.[217]

PUT IT INTO ACTION: EXERCISES FOR POINT 6

1. **Start now.** There's no time like the present—start eating the Brain Tune Up way. During your next "me" time, make a

list of ways you could make healthier food choices. Your list might include items like "eat fish twice a week" or "cook with olive oil." Choose three to put into place immediately.

2. Set SMART Goals. Spend some time setting goals for your new way of eating, and remember to think in terms of breaking things down into manageable tasks. Perhaps your goal is to eat fish twice a week but you don't know how to cook it. One of your sub goals might then be to research recipes for cooking fish.

3. Visualize. Utilize your meditation time to visualize yourself following the Brain Tune Up eating plan. See, hear, feel and smell this new kind of eating, and the brand new you that will result.

4. Choose one new food per week. Experiment! Select a different food or recipe to try each week, something you've never had before. This can be fun for you and the loved one you are caring for.

Point 7: Hydration

Water is, quite literally, the elixir of life. You've heard a million times how important water is for you, and you probably also know that you should drink eight glasses a day. But do you? If not, would it motivate you to know that water is essential for the efficient functioning of your brain?

WATER FACTS AND FIGURES

Take a look around the internet, and you'll find all kinds of information about hydration. To be honest, much of it is controversial. You can find the following statistics listed as fact on multiple websites:

- 75% of Americans are chronically dehydrated. Not only that, researchers estimate that probably 50% of the population of the entire world is also chronically dehydrated.

- 37% of Americans have such a weak thirst mechanism that they mistake it for hunger.

- Mild dehydration can slow down your metabolism by 3%. Imagine what chronic dehydration does.

- Nearly 100% of dieters in a University of Washington study had hunger pangs satisfied by drinking a glass of water.

- Insufficient water is the leading cause of daytime fatigue.

- Up to 80% of back and joint-pain sufferers could have their pain eased by drinking eight to ten glasses of water a day.

- Even a 2% drop in body water can trigger short-term memory loss, trouble doing basic math, and difficulties in focusing.

- Drinking five glasses of water a day decreases the risk of colon cancer by 45%, decreases the risk of breast cancer by 79%, and bladder cancer by 50%.

However, not all doctors and medical authorities agree with these assessments. The one thing that we do know is that our bodies need water but can't store it so it is essential to replace fluids every day.[218]

I've observed from years of working with patients in my private practice that the human body and brain function best with six to eight glasses of water a day.

So, after reading all of this are you starting to get thirsty? Good. I'll wait while you go get yourself a nice, big cool glass of water. Okay? While you sip it, I'll tell you first why water is so important for your body, and then why it is so good for your brain.

WATER AND THE BODY

You may be surprised to learn that water is *the* most crucial nutrient in your body. Over half of you is comprised of water, that's right; the average adult consists of 50% to 65% water.[219] And what really makes it the most crucial is that humans can only live a matter of days without it! Consider this: every system in our body uses and relies on water. It transports nutrients and oxygen to our cells, protects our organs and tissues, lubricates joints, regulates our body temperature and flushes toxins.[220]

In fact, our blood is made up of 83% water.[221] This is important because blood transports nutrients throughout our bodies and moves waste products to be excreted. So without adequate water, our bodies not only starve, but are poisoned with the waste products that cannot be expelled.[222]

Our blood carries waste products to our kidneys, after which is expelled from the body through our urine. If the body senses there isn't enough water available, however, it reacts by retaining what water it has already. What happens next is that this stored water gets contaminated with waste. Why? Because the kidneys have no way to release the toxins.

When this occurs, the job of clearing waste shifts to the liver, which is already working hard to clean out other substances from our blood. When it takes on some of the work of the kidney, the liver can't work as efficiently. And guess what one of the liver's most important jobs is? Burning fat. So when it is overloaded the stored fat can't be burned and the body will hold onto what water it has. Thus, weight gain occurs.[223]

We've already discussed the links between obesity and Alzheimer's, and so losing weight is an excellent goal for

reasons of health and vanity. Drinking adequate water every day
can help you lose the weight, besides all the other benefits it has for your body.

How Much Water Do I Use?

Every day, the average adult loses approximately 2.5 liters of water through sweating, elimination, and breathing.[224] This breaks down as follows:

- 300 ml from the lungs, through breathing
- 1500 ml excreted by kidneys as urine
- 200 ml from the gastrointestinal tract
- 500 ml through the skin in perspiration and other evaporation[225]

As we've seen, this loss of water must be replaced, or the body's organs begin to not function correctly. A very small amount of water per day, around 200 ml, is produced by the body through metabolic reactions. This leaves a deficit of 2300 ml.[226]

Exercise

And these figures are just for the body as it goes about its day to day business. There are certain activities such as exercise that use up even more water. With exercise the exertion of the muscles is amplified, increasing the need for oxygen. To regulate body temperature and to allow the oxygen to get to the muscles, sweat production and respiration rate are also increased. This in turn results in more water loss from the lungs.[227] Clearly, you will need to increase your water intake during exercise.

Thirst Sensation

Older people lose their ability to distinguish thirst cues, and so it is also vitally important to make sure your loved one is drinking enough water. Seniors can be vulnerable to dehydration because of diminishing thirst centers.[228]

Researchers have recently discovered a unique region in the brain that appears to regulate the human body's need for water. This region is called the mid cingulate cortex, and its function is to predict how much water a person needs. Scientists have also discovered that this area of the brain tends to malfunction in older people. Researchers gave old (age 65-74) people and young (age 21-30) people salt water in order to make them thirsty, and afterwards allowed each group to drink as much water as they wanted. The older people drank half as much as the younger group, and brain imaging found that the mid cingulate cortex was turned off earlier.[229]

How Much Water Do I Need?

My recommendation for water consumption is six, eight ounce glasses of water a day. (See the tips section later in this chapter for ideas on how to drink your water.) The World Health Organization recommends drinking six to eight large glasses of water a day.[230] However, the National Institute of Medicine recommends that women drink nine glasses a day, and men drink thirteen glasses.[231]

While this amount of water will be adequate for your loved one, bear in mind that these recommendations are designed to aid in normal fluid balance. They do not take into account the extra need for water that exercise will place on your body, or the demands of a hot day.[232]

It may be helpful to learn the signs that indicate a body is getting enough water. They are, either pale yellow or colorless urine; quenched thirst; and feeling well.[233]

When Do I Need More Water?

This is important, so let me repeat it: drinking six glasses of water a day is a minimum recommendation for normal fluid balance. There are other conditions that would cause your body to need even more water. These situations are:

- **Illness.** Certain illnesses and health problems can make your body lose fluids and therefore require special attention to rehydrating. These are conditions such as vomiting, diarrhea, fever, infections and wounds.

- **Variations in the weather.** It stands to reason that you should drink more water in hot weather, since you are sweating more. However, be aware that cold weather can require more fluid intake also. Wearing layers of warm clothing can cause increased sweat, and heated indoor air also causes moisture loss.

- **High altitude.** Any altitude over 8,200 feet increases your body's respiration and urination, and this in turn increases the amount of water your body needs.

- **Exercise.** As we have seen, exercise increases your body's need for water dramatically. Drink two cups of water two hours before exercising, then one-half cup for every fifteen minutes of exercise.

- **Pregnancy.** Remember, you're drinking for two! Aim to consume ten glasses of water a day. During nursing, you should ingest thirteen glasses each day.[234]

WATER AND THE BRAIN

You've just learned that the human body is made up of 50%-65% water. If this surprised you, get ready for a shocker—your brain is comprised of 75% water! Drinking adequate water is just as important for the health of the brain as it is for the health of our bodies. Your brain needs plenty of glucose, oxygen, water and other essential nutrients to function well.

If your brain doesn't get enough water, you might feel dizzy, fatigued and get a headache, and you'll start to lose your ability to concentrate. Studies have shown that a glass of water every hour while studying prevents fatigue and headaches.

Optimal Brain Performance

Because your brain is 75% water, ample hydration is an absolute must. When the water in your brain decreases, stress hormones are released. These hormones block glucose, which is the primary fuel of the brain, from entering brain cells. This in turn results in memory problems.

It is important to understand that even a minor amount of dehydration can raise stress hormones in the brain and damage your brain over time. Remember, also, that your blood is constantly delivering nutrients to the brain and removing toxins. Blood is made up mostly of water, as we have seen, and this is another reason why water is so important for your brain.

MYELIN

A lack of water can cause demyelination in the cells of the brain. I told you about neurogenesis in Point 5, exercise, and that humans are now understood to create new nerve endings and brain cells throughout their lives. There's an important substance in the brain called myelin that is part of these nerve endings, and drinking water is important to them, too.

Myelin insulates the nerve fibers and sends messages from brain cell to brain. Damaged myelin causes the formation of plaques implicated in Alzheimer's. The main function of the myelin in your brain is to speed impulses along the nerves. Thus, when the myelin is damaged, thinking slows.

Demyelination occurs when the insulation around the nerves breaks down. With injured myelin in the brain, nerve transmission slows and eventually the brain cell deteriorates and loses function.

Why all this worry about myelin in a chapter on hydration? Because, you guessed it, dehydration can damage the brain and it's myelin.

DEHYDRATION

What exactly is dehydration? Dehydration is characterized by "the excessive loss of water from the body." It is a condition that can become a major problem connected with illnesses, such as problems in the gastrointestinal tract, nausea and vomiting. The effects of certain medications can also deplete fluids. Dehydration can become so serious that it can be fatal.[235]

Signs of Dehydration

It is important to pay attention to any signs that you may be dehydrated. It is especially important to be watchful for dehydration in your senior loved ones, because as we have seen, our elders often do not drink enough water. Be wary of these signs:

- Having a dry mouth
- Being Tired
- Muscle weakness and/or cramps
- Being delirious
- Decreased urine output
- Lack of sweating
- Headache
- Being dizzy or lightheaded
- Low blood pressure or rapid heartbeat[236]

Treatment for Dehydration

The best treatment for dehydration is prevention. But if it does occur, begin hydration with fluids if possible. If there has been excessive fluid loss due to the effects of an illness, intravenous fluid hydration may be required. Contact your doctor if you have any worries whatsoever—dehydration is nothing to take lightly.[237]

TIPS FOR DRINKING ENOUGH WATER

Drinking lots of water is a habit that you can develop, just like eating right and exercising. Yes, drinking all this water every day will make you urinate more. But, bear in mind that urination is how the body gets rid of all those nasty toxins. Going to the bathroom more often has huge health benefits in the long run. Every time you run to the bathroom, be aware of all the toxins you are releasing. [238] Try these tips to increase your water consumption:

- If you have not been in the habit of drinking much water, increase slowly.

- When you first increase your water intake, you may actually feel thirstier! But this will soon pass as your body gets accustomed to being properly hydrated.

- As your body gets used to having enough water, the feeling of having to urinate will decrease. This may be difficult to accept during the first few days of drinking a lot of water, but it is indeed so![249]

- Drink water in the morning, so that it doesn't disrupt your sleep (Point 4).

- Buy a six-pack of eight ounce bottles and to remind yourself to drink one an hour, label them: 6 AM, 7 AM, 8 AM, 9 AM, 10 AM, 11 AM,

- Save money and waste by refilling the bottles for the next day.

- If you don't like water, try putting lemon juice in it.

PUT IT INTO ACTION: EXERCISES FOR POINT 7

1. Create a system for drinking six glasses of water.

Will you buy a six-pack of bottles and label them? Refill the bottles or stock a fresh supply? If you are environmentally conscious, you might want to purchase a water filter for your kitchen faucet, or water pitcher. There are also companies which will deliver water to your home.

2. How do you like your water?

Do you like it ice cold from the refrigerator or at room temperature? If you are keeping your bottled water in the frig, but have a hard time drinking it when it's cold, you won't drink your quota. Do you prefer it with lemon in it? Or perhaps a twist of lime? Figure out how best you like it and then drink it that way.

3. How will you track your consumption?

This is important to consider for you and your loved one. Will you create a chart that you can mark off? Use the Bresky labeled bottle system described above? Pour your daily quota into a pre-measured container and then drink it all? Choose a plan and stick with it.

Point 8: Brain Exercises and Art Rx

If you are caring for a loved one with dementia or any kind of diminished brain function, you may be eager to learn ways in which you can prevent the loss of your own cognitive abilities. That may even be one reason that you are reading this book. The good news is that you've come to the right place—there are many things that you can do for yourself and your family. There are also activities you can get your loved one with dementia to participate in that will have a big impact on their brain.

My Brain Tune Up program is designed to assist you to make changes in your lifestyle that will increase the brain power of both you and the loved one that you care for. I've shown you many things you can do for your body in previous chapters. Together, we have looked at the benefits of fun, relaxation, music, sleep, exercise, diet and hydration. And along the way, I've shown how these important habits also beneficially affect your brain.

But now it is time for the brain to take center stage all on its own. Would you be interested if I told you that there are numerous simple ways to give your brain a mental workout that will help improve the function and health of your brain and prevent dementia?

If you've seen first-hand the effects of diminished brain ability, no doubt your answer would be yes. The good news is that these mental exercises can also be adapted for use by your loved one. Just as it is never too late to begin exercising, it's never too late to give your brain a workout, too.

The latest scientific research indicates the following results that can be gained by mental exercises:

- Better memory
- Increased ability to concentrate
- Faster, clearer thought processes
- Improved awareness and responsiveness

Because our population is living longer, taking action to reduce or delay cognitive decline is imperative. Especially, since these changes happen in everyone to some degree, even the healthiest among us.

In Point 6, I cited some alarming statistics about the expected increase in the incidence of Alzheimer's within our population. Any improvement in dealing with Alzheimer's would be welcome, but studies have shown that if we could delay the onset of Alzheimer's by five years, it would dramatically reduce the impact of this disease on society.[240]

Currently, over 100 billion dollars (yes, you read those figures correctly) is spent every year on dementia. This equals 10% of all healthcare expenditures.[241] The best way to treat dementia is to prevent it in the first place. We've looked at the critical impact of a high-fat diet, inactivity, and stress as factors in developing Alzheimer's. But other important factors are social and mental activities.

The world's leading neurologists, scientists, medical journals and newspapers report that daily brain exercise will slow memory decline.

I underlined this because I've had the good fortune of watching my patients change right before my eyes as their memories and overall happiness improve doing my brain exercises and my Art Rx. It's very pleasing to see the medical community is researching and reporting this wonderful fact. It further substantiates and brings public acceptance to the work we've had the great pleasure of providing in my medical practice over the past decade.

Researchers in these studies learned that mental and social activities boost memory function and may build the brain's cognitive reserve.

Building Your Brain Bank or Cognitive Reserve

What is cognitive reserve? It is the brain's ability to perform and thrive, even in the face of problems associated with memory impairment. Recent studies show participating in mental activities allows brain cells to establish new connections. These new connections work to protect brain cells from possible "bankruptcy" or harm. Scientists call this cognitive reserve, or what I like to say we're "building your brain bank" to defend against memory deterioration. I encourage my patients to make a deposit in their brain bank daily by performing brain exercises. It is also now thought that these mental activities actually stimulate the creation of new brain cells. Not only that, but if some cells have died off due to brain disease, an abundance of new cells from the brain's own stem cells may grow in their place.[242]

Below are just some of the recent studies reporting the importance of regular mentally stimulating activities along with good social interaction:

Columbia University Study Results:

Studies have shown that seniors, who do crossword puzzles, attend classes, play card games or read books and newspapers may be less likely to develop Alzheimer's. These results came from a Columbia University study. Researchers followed 283 men and women with an average age of 79, all of whom had been diagnosed with Alzheimer's disease.

The activities tracked were:

- **Social activities** such as volunteer work; going to movies or sporting events, or attending a social center

- **Physical activities** such as walking and exercising

- **Intellectual activities** such as attending classes, playing cards or bingo, and reading books, magazines and newspapers

- **Other activities** such as listening to music or watching TV[243]

The Nun Study Results

The most comprehensive study to date regarding the positive effects of mentally stimulating activities is the famous Nun study. This study has followed and tracked the daily activities of more than 600 nuns for the past two decades. The nuns volunteered to donate their brains after their death for research purposes. The initial findings from the autopsies indicate the nuns who continued to perform mentally stimulating activities delayed the onset of dementia symptoms. Autopsy results from a number of these "active" nuns showed brain deterioration associated with Alzheimer's, but amazingly they showed no noticeable signs of memory loss during their lifetime.[244]

The JAMA Study and More

The Journal of American Medical Association found in a similar study, "results suggest that frequent participation in cognitively stimulating activities is associated with reduced risk of Alzheimer's disease."[245]

Other studies have shown that continuing to enjoy leisure activities throughout life reduces the risk of developing Alzheimer's. So the old saying, "use it or lose it," is indeed true. All adults should continue to participate in activities they've enjoyed during their lives, whether it's playing cards, or other games, or being social with family and friends.[246]

Rush University Study Results (The Loneliness and Boredom Factor)

A Rush University Medical Center study reported that lonely people have a greater possibility of developing cognitive decline. In the study of 823 people, those classified as lonely were twice as likely to develop dementia. Yes, *twice* as likely.[247]

Also, if you are not challenging yourself daily, this can lead to boredom, which can lead to anxiety, depression and problems with attention and concentration. Thus, it is important to become a life-long learner, and don't forget that one important way we learn is through games and leisure activities.

If you fear that your loved one is becoming lonely or bored, it is important to stop the downward spiral now. Their mind depends on it. Right away, you need to find ways to provide or participate in enjoyable, actionable activities. Here are some sound, simple suggestions I found in a recent guideline on *Non-pharmacologic management of agitated behaviors*: first, you can create activities based on your loved one's personal

130

history. So, if your father was a textile salesperson for many years, perhaps he would like to match fabric squares. If your mother was a decorator, you could show her photos of rooms and talk about what activities would go on in them.

Here is a list of other possible activities:

- Cleaning tasks
- Laundry tasks
- Cooking (may require supervision)
- Potting flowers or plants
- Self-expression such as music, painting, drawing, working with clay
- Reminiscing (can be done alone or in a group)
- Life Review (a more structured way of reminiscing)
- Card playing (suited to the loved one's level of ability)[248]

Effectiveness of Brain Exercises to "Build Your Brain Bank"

You'll find a helpful compendium of brain exercises and suggestions for mental activities at the end of this chapter, but right now I want to share with you why they are so important.

Recently, one of the largest studies ever conducted on aging and cognitive training was done at the University of Southern California Andrus Gerontology Center. It showed that brain exercise increased participants ability to remember useful, everyday information and enhanced their communication abilities and self-confidence.[249]

The Journal of the American Medical Association published a study that showed that mental exercises can slow the progression of cognitive decline by five years.[250] This can cut the incidence of Alzheimer's by 50%![251]

Brain Tune Up® Study Results

And let me share with you the results of one of my own studies conducted at the Jewish Home for the Aging in Reseda, California. Funded by a grant from the Jewish Community Foundation, the study ran from October 2005 through March 2006. First, I trained the staff for one month on all 9 Points of the Brain Tune Up. This was to ensure that they could assist the participants in the study, who were on average 90 years old, with the Brain Tune Up.

An independent social worker conducted all testing and found remarkable results. On memory tests, the average person over 90 years old *loses* 1 point every 6 months without intervention. In this study some of the highlights were:

- One male participant, aged 94, increased 2 points

- One female participant, aged 95, increased 1 point

- Overall there was an average increase in scores of 30%

The best results of all were with the Global Quality of Life Scale, which reported increases of 25% to 46%. Self-reports from participants found 67% improvement over 5 or more areas.

It is so exciting for me to see the results of studies such as these because it proves that at any age (even 90!) the Brain Tune Up, works! Like exercising your muscles, the brain needs exercise too.

Art Rx

The <u>code</u> for the brain's stimulation is numbers (left side) and patterns (right side) and therefore all of the cognitive and attention training brain exercises I've designed revolve around utilization of this code.

One of the activities I've developed is the Art Rx exercises. These become favorites among my patients, because the drawing exercises give them a sense of mastery and make them feel like someone special again.

Many patients are hesitant to begin the Art Rx sessions. They say things like, "I've never drawn before." What I say to them in return is simple: "Good. It's time you start." I don't allow them any excuses because I know how beneficial the Art Rx activities are to brain health.

To get people drawing, I use a grid system based on Michelangelo's work from 500 years ago, and a layering system. This involves beginning with a general outline, and with each new layer, adding in more detail. These exercises produce drawings that constantly surprise my patients. They are impressed with their new skills! After they've produced a drawing, I have them sign and date it—and then send it to their families. In this way, these elderly citizens no longer feel invisible.

For more information on Art Rx, including easy-to-follow instructions for duplicating the exercises please see the Brain Tune Up® Brain Exercise and Art Rx workbooks.

Revisiting Neurogenesis

I first told you about the exciting field of neurogenesis back in Point 5, when we were looking at the benefits of physical exercise to the brain. To review, neurogenesis is the field which studies the birth of neurons in the brain.

For many years, scientists and brain researchers felt that no new brain cells are created as we grow. It was thought that humans are born with a set number of cells. But now we have learned that our miraculous human brains grow new brain cells all throughout our lives. Princeton University scientists reported in 1999 that new neurons grow in several regions of the cerebral cortex that have to do with cognitive and perceptual functions.

It was also found that the ravages of stress on the brain can be reversed. Healing took place when marmosets were taken out of their cages and placed in an enclosed environment with hidden food to search for, a variety of toys, and plants and branches to sit on. The brains of the marmosets expanded with new cells. The mind is much like a muscle in that it swells with exercise. Thus, enriched environments are essential for all ages. It is simple—activating the brain fights stress.[252]

Brain Plasticity

Currently, much discussion between memory experts is regarding brain plasticity or neuroplasticity. It doesn't have anything to do with plastic, but has everything to do with the power of our brains to restructure itself as we learn something new or create new experiences. The reason it is important is scientists use this term to describe the brain's capacity to create and recreate new pathways and networks through learning new ideas. Challenging your mind with new tasks and skills helps redesign the brain's shape. Through repetition and good habits the brain reconnects and rewires itself at any age. Eventually, this positive replication of learning and new skills will improve the storage of memory in an aging brain.[253]

More Studies on Cognitive Reserve

I already mentioned that "cognitive reserve" is the concept that a brain can store up a defense or reserve against memory loss. Although brain scans and autopsies may show all the visible signs of Alzheimer's, many active seniors may have built up enough cognitive reserve to never show the behavioral signs of memory deterioration. Studies are confirming people who stay active, live purposeful lives, challenge their brains and continue to set goals can build a cognitive reserve that keeps them from showing normal signs of memory loss, even though their brains physically show an abundance of Alzheimer's related brain plaques.

Academy of Neurology Study Results

Until recently, cognitive reserve was only theory. However, as recently as April 15, 2008 the Academy of Neurology announced a study which validated that people who remain mentally sharp well into their 80's and beyond had a 20% larger hippocampal region of their brain compared to similar inactive seniors in the study. The study showed the brains of active seniors have a larger hippocampus because they remain mentally sharp and alert. During the study, autopsies were performed upon death and showed many of the "active" seniors had the dreaded Alzheimer's plaques, but never showed the Alzheimer's behavior during their lifetime. The concept of cognitive reserve adds more reason to stay alert, be a life-long learner, and keep your brain lively and active. By "building your brain bank" and staying mentally active you may build up high levels of cognitive reserve and grow your brain's hippocampus.[254]

Recent studies have also discovered that both well-educated people and those in high-level jobs have a better chance of preventing mental deterioration in late life. No, this doesn't mean you have to be rich and smart to ward off memory loss. It means these educated, hard working people had a lifestyle that demanded they perform mentally stimulating activities over a sustained period of time. People with active lifestyles possibly built up cognitive reserve which blocked memory decline. By strengthening brain networks and developing new brain connections, they preserved memory and attention. The point is we all must continue to stay active and challenge our brains in order to build cognitive reserve.[255]

Tools for Brain Health

Have I convinced you of the importance of mental exercises and leisure activities to brain health? I thought so. And now

135

you are probably anxious to get to the exercises. Let me remind you of one critical fact: brain exercises and activities are important for you *and* your loved one. Following the activities I suggest will improve the quality of your loved one's life dramatically. If you take part in them you'll lower your risk for dementia and Alzheimer's. It's a win-win situation for both of you. So let's get started.

Have a Young Attitude. Learn a new skill. Cultivate intensity. Shun the tried and true; the already mastered skills. Accept the challenge of mastering something new.[256] This has the effect of making you joyous and vital, which in turn attracts other people to you. And that is important not only because it makes life more pleasant, but also because of the next Point.

High Levels of Oxytocin Increases Brain Power. Oxytocin is a hormone sometimes called the "trust hormone" and high levels of it increases your brain's ability to think of new solutions to a problem.[257] The good news is cuddling, sex and chocolate cause the body to release chemicals that stimulate the production of oxytocin.

Pleasure in the Body Enables High Brain Performance. Pleasure in the body means laughter (Point 1), involvement with others and in life, satisfaction, and yes, sex. Spend time with people whose company you like. Enjoy social interactions with other positive people. Share a joke and a laugh with your friends. This also means, of course, that it's a good idea to avoid negative people. The health of your brain depends on it.[258]

Learn Memory Tools. Mastering a couple of simple ways to remember things can help build up your cognitive reserves. Repetitive brain exercises and memory activities are an excellent way to build your brain. See the exercise section at the end of this chapter for a good memory tool.

There are two kinds of memory, short-term and long-term. Short-term memory lasts up to two hours. In order for something to be transferred from short-term memory to long-term memory, you need to pay attention to it with your eyes and ears for nine seconds. This is especially important for older people to practice, as they have a difficult time multi-tasking. After that, the information will be placed in your long-term memory if the information is repeated five times a day OUT LOUD for five days in a row.

Engage in Mentally-Stimulating Activities. These include gardening, taking classes, volunteering, working crosswords or other kinds of puzzles, learning a language, whatever tickles your fancy! Working a crossword puzzle lowers your risk of Alzheimer's by 67%. As we have seen, these activities exercise your brain and guard against dementia.

Be Creative! It is often actually easier to free one's creative spirit with age. Seniors no longer need to worry about selling their art, or what people think. Creativity can be as simple as enjoying a beautiful day in the sun. Being present in the moment can be a joyously creative activity.[259]

Art Rx. Refer to the previous discussion in this chapter (or the Brain Tune Up® Brain Exercises and Art Rx Workbooks) for specific exercises you and your loved one can do to engage your brain. Not only that, the Art Rx activities also grow new brain cells. Can't beat that combination!

As you can see, there are dozens if not hundreds of activities in which you can participate that will help with your brain health. The key is to choose something that you love. Just as in Point 1, Laughter, and Point 3, Tunes Rx, it doesn't matter what you decide to participate in as long as you do it. Play cards, study a language, learn about a new culture, paint a picture, solve a puzzle—there are so many fun and challenging activities in the world! Remember, to grow new dendrites (the extensions of a neuron that send and receive nerve impulses) in your brain, you must do new, exciting, challenging, intellectual work every day.

Go forth and do them. And see the following exercise section for more specific suggestions.

PUT IT INTO ACTION: EXERCISES FOR POINT 8

1. Review this Brain Exercises section.

Decide which exercises you might like and make a list. Next time you have a few extra minutes—while waiting for your loved one at the doctor's office, for instance—do one of the things on your list. Work a crossword or sudoku puzzle. Study a new topic. Exercise your creativity—draw what you see around you.

Here's another easy one to practice with your loved one. Instead of following the same morning ritual when you wake up, use the "switch sides" exercise. The "switch sides" exercise is simply switching hands when you brush your hair or teeth. Or if you use your right hand to eat breakfast, switch to the left hand. Repeatedly challenge your brain to switch from using the right hemisphere to the left hemisphere by challenging the brain to change its routine and learn a new skill. Repetition is the key.

2. Cultivate an attitude of intense curiosity.

Be curious about the world. If something catches your fancy, learn more about it. Doesn't matter if it is studying the political situation in Africa, or learning the Latin names of the flowers you like to plant. Follow your curiosity wherever it leads you.

3. Do memory exercises.

Here is a good one:

Follow the BRAVO Method. What is BRAVO? It is an easy to remember mnemonic device. (Mnemosyne was the Greek God of Memory).

Bright
Repetition
Association
Visualization
Organization

All you need to do is remember the word BRAVO, which will remind you to be bright, lively, and curious; repeat what you want to remember; associate it with something else; visualize it for a few seconds; and organize these tools in your mind.

Point 9: Kindness

"My religion is simple. My religion is kindness." The Dalai Lama.

What I'm about to tell you in this chapter may surprise you more than anything else I've talked about in this book. Are you ready? Here is the startling fact: one of the most important routes to health is through kindness.

Yes, kindness.

It may seem almost too simplistic to believe that practicing acts of kindness on a daily basis can have a huge positive impact on your brain health. But it's true, and I have the studies and research to prove it.

One of the greatest things about kindness is its simplicity. We all know what kindness is, right? It is, plain and simple, being nice to each other. What could be simpler than that?

Performing an act of kindness means you have given the gift of yourself and your time to another being. (As a caregiver you are in the perfect position to do this.)

I'm not the first person to say this, and I certainly won't be the last, but the strength of the message remains the same no matter who says it:

Give your most precious asset, TIME, to others.

Make giving time to others your kindness motto, as it is mine. It is just that easy—but we humans make it complicated. We say we don't have time to give to others, or we are afraid to put ourselves out. Yet there are numerous small but effective kindnesses that you can perform easily and in a small amount of time. (We'll look at some of those at the end of this chapter.)

What I'm talking about is the Golden Rule. You remember it: "Do unto others as you would have them do unto you." When you are kind and helpful and fair to people, they have a tendency to treat you the same way. We've all heard the old saying, "what goes around comes around." It is a saying that has lasted because it is true. It may interest you to know that all of the great religious traditions prescribe a variant of the Golden Rule.

Let's have a look at some of them:

- **Baha'i**: "Lay not on any soul a load that you would not wish to be laid upon you, and desire not for anyone the things you would not desire for yourself" Baha'u'llah, Gleanings

- **Buddhism:** "Hurt not others in ways that you yourself would find hurtful" Udana-Varga, 5:18

- **Christianity**: "Therefore all things whatsoever ye would that men should do to you, do ye even so to them:

for this is the law and the prophets" Matthew 7:12, King James Version.

- **Confucianism:** "Do not do to others what you do not want them to do to you" Analects 15:23

- **Hinduism:** "This is the sum of duty: do not do to others what would cause you pain if done to you" Mahabharata 5.1517

- **Islam:** "No one of you is a believer until he desires for his brother that which he desires for himself" Sunnah

- **Judaism**: "What is hateful to you, do not to your fellow man. That is the entire law. And the rest is commentary" Talmud, Shabbat 31a

- **Sikhism**: "Don't create enmity with anyone as God is within everyone" Guru Arjan Devji 259

But you don't have to be the least bit religious to adhere to the idea of the Golden Rule. Perhaps you shy away from organized religion for personal reasons. It is still possible— and preferable—to be ethical. Bear in mind that ethics and religion have the same basic principles, these are of service, dignity, honor, and compassion.

Kindness breeds happiness, and both are good for your health! In order to aid you in your quest for happiness, here are some rules that can be found in inspirational writings throughout the world.

Remember the five simple rules to be happy:
1. Free your heart from hatred
2. Free your mind from worries
3. Live simply
4. Give more
5. Expect less.

Rule #4—giving more—is the basis of kindness.

It doesn't take a lot to extend an act of kindness, and with a little thought you can easily incorporate it into your day. Kindness is a way of thinking, and once you begin to think about kindness, it snowballs. Not only will you want to do more, but the others to whom you extend kindness will want to also. Remember also that kindness is important to the loved one you care for, not only in you being kind to them, but in them finding ways that they can perform acts of kindness in their own lives.

Now I want to spend a little time telling you why being kind is such a good idea for your brain health.

Health Benefits of Kindness

Lest you think that giving to others—whether it is your time or your money—cannot possibly make you happier, I beg to differ. Here's some evidence.

A study published in the journal *Science* reported that people who give to charities have a higher level of happiness than those who don't. Researchers at the University of British Columbia and Harvard University wanted to find out if how people spend their money affects their happiness. The basic finding of the study was that giving to others, whether it was volunteering time or donating money, made people happy.[260]

Dr. Larry Dossey calls the good effects a person gets from contributing to others the "helper's high," and says it benefits the person giving the help as well as receiving it. Not only that, it may even benefit people who witness the helping even from a distance![261]

One person who has done a great deal of research into the impact of kindness of our emotional and physical health is Allan Luks, who, along with Peggy Payne, wrote *The Healing Power of Doing Good* in 1991.[262] Luks began his investigation after noticing how good he felt when he was kind to others. He was surprised to learn that many others felt the same way, and he eventually wrote his book about it. Luks noticed an entire catalog of beneficial effects that came from acts of kindness. They include:

- Happier outlook on life
- More optimistic outlook on life
- Increased energy
- Exhilaration and euphoria
- Increased feeling of being healthy
- Higher sense of well being
- Feeling of being connected with others
- More calm and relaxation
- Increased longevity
- Less insomnia
- Stronger immune system
- Less pain
- Healthier cardiovascular system
- Increased body warmth
- Asthma relief
- Arthritis relief
- Reduced cancer activity
- Faster recovery from surgery[263]

That's a darn good laundry list of results!

But *why*, precisely, does kindness help? One reason is because doing something for others takes you out of yourself. When you are doing something nice for someone else, you're thinking about them, not you. The focus is taken off your problems. Another reason, according to Harvard cardiologist Dr. Herbert Benson, is that your body rewards you with euphoric sensations from releasing endorphins, and this in turn boosts your self confidence. Dr. Paul Pearsall, a psychologist who wrote *The Pleasure Prescription*, notes that this is an example of the body biologically rewarding us for doing good.[264]

The above, mentioned Allan Luks conducted a study of over 3000 volunteers nationwide. The study was a survey which asked volunteers how they felt when they did something kind. In analyzing the results of the survey, Luks found a clear link between helping others and good health. One of the main reactions that volunteers reported was a big drop in their stress level, with over 90% of respondents enjoying this benefit.[265]

One of the earliest studies to gain attention for discovering the link between helping others and good health was reported in a 1977 book by psychiatrist George Vaillant. The book, called *Adaptation to Life*, detailed the results of a 30-year study of Harvard graduates. Vaillant compared the relative levels of health in men in their fifties with their attitudinal biases. He concluded that a lifestyle filled with kindness and altruism was crucial to good mental health.[266] Another study from Michigan that spanned ten years and followed 2,700 men, found that those who volunteered regularly lowered their death rates by two and a half times versus non-volunteers.[267]

Suggestions for Acts of Kindness

So, the evidence is clear—kindness is good for everyone. But what if you have gotten out of the habit of kindness and need some suggestions? Never fear, help is on the way. Check out this list of possible activities.

- Take home-baked brownies to a shut-in
- Take an elderly parent out for lunch
- Volunteer to take a senior friend grocery shopping
- Walk a dog for a neighbor
- Talk to the other seniors at your loved one's care center

- Take flowers, cookies or treats to the staff at the care center
- Choose a book to share with your loved one and read a chapter every visit
- Watch a movie with a shut-in or elderly neighbor
- Donate to your favorite charity
- Tell your family how much you love them
- Pay for coffee for the person in line behind you at Starbucks
- Write a thank you note to a loved one, just because
- Volunteer to baby-sit for a young couple who might not otherwise get out

There are so many simple, easy ways to perform acts of kindness. These are just a few ideas to get you started. You'll think of many more as you get in the kindness habit. Remember, it is important for the person you are caring for to get into the kindness habit, too, so adapt some of these ideas for them.

If you need more ideas, consult the following websites (and be sure to read some of the inspiring stories you'll find on them):

Help Others.org, www.helpothers.org

Blossom International, www.blossominternational.org

Great Deeds, www.greatdeeds.org

The Random Acts of Kindness Foundation, www.randomactsofkindness.org

Acts of kindness, www.actsofkindness.com

The Pay it Forward Foundation, www.payitforwardfoundation.org

Extreme Kindness, www.extremekindness.com

You'll find enough ideas and inspiration on these sites to keep you busy activating your kindness muscle for a long time!

"If you do this, you will live many years, and your life will be satisfying. Never let loyalty and **kindness** leave you! Tie them around your neck as a reminder. Write them deep within your heart. Then you will find favor with both God and people, and you will earn a good reputation."
-Proverbs 3:2-4

PUT IT INTO ACTION: EXERCISES FOR POINT 9

1. Just do it.

Often the best acts of kindness are the spontaneous ideas that occur during the course of our day to day lives—helping an older woman lift her carry-on luggage to the overhead compartment, assisting a blind person across a busy street, holding the door open for a mother pushing a stroller. Don't hang back in these situations—jump in and perform a simple act of kindness.

2. Make a kindness list.

As you may have noticed by now, I'm a great fan of list making, because it is a way to be prepared. Write down your favorite ideas for acts of kindness. Visit the websites listed and start your list. Add your own ideas to it. This way you always have your ideas organized and ready to refer to.

Conclusion

We've taken quite a journey together, you and I, and I hope that you have enjoyed it as much as I have. I get so excited talking about my Brain Tune Up 9 Pt. System, because I know how vitally important it is for the health and well-being of not only our senior citizens, but their caregivers as well.

I believe that every human on the planet should have the right to enjoy wonderful, glowing health, of the body, spirit and the brain. With advances in medical science furthering our understanding of what it takes to be healthy more and more every day, this goal is within reach.

What is the best way to achieve this optimum health? You have been reading the answer to that question. Following my Brain Tune Up 9 Pt. System regularly will boost your health and improve the health of your loved one as well. You'll both be happier and enjoy the time you spend together, rather than being laden with worry, stress, and resentment.

All it takes for caregivers and their loved ones to thrive are following 9 simple Points:

1. Fun and Laughter
2. Relaxation, Meditation and Prayer
3. Tunes Rx
4. Sleep
5. Physical Exercise
6. Brain Tune Up® Eating Plan
7. Hydration
8. Brain Exercises and Art Rx
9. Kindness

My 9 Point System is a way of life that will bring you joy and happiness as well as satisfaction and vitality. Using the correct evidence-based conditions, a person of any age can improve memory, concentration and mental sharpness. It is important for every person to learn about and take advantage of the

148

scientific breakthroughs for people with memory problems. These are problems associated with age, stress and sleep deprivation. Start implementing these suggestions today and you'll notice a difference immediately.

Epilogue

One of my key philosophies of life is that it is good for society when our elderly enjoy a high quality of life. In the light of the marvelous developments of modern medicine, good brain health and caregiving excellence are now possible. Wisdom tells us it is not how long we live, but how well we live.

You can indeed be the Captain of your ship of fate. You can make things happen and not just let things happen to you. We all have to enjoy whole-person wellness, gratefulness and kindness to have more meaning and purpose in life. Today, make the choice to maintain and reclaim your brain health as you age gracefully and successfully. Make the choice every day. Make this promise to yourself and to your caregiving recipient and keep that promise.

If you need more caregiving skills or tools please visit **www.mybraintuneup.com.**

Arnold Bresky, M.D.
Preventive Gerontologist
(310) 282-9937

National Resource Telephone Numbers

Senior Centers and Aging Network Services
- Administration on Aging [eldercare locator]: 1-800-677-1116
- National Association on State Units of Aging: 1-202-898-2578

Continuum of Services
- Eldercare Locator- 1-800-677-1116

Specific Senior Services
- ABA Commission of Legal problems of the Elderly- 1-202-662-8690
- Assisted Living Foundation of America- 1-703-894-1805
- National Alliance for the Mentally Ill- 1-800-950-6264
- National Association of Home Care- 1-202-547-7424
- National Hospice Foundation- 1-703-516-4928

Specific Diseases
- Alzheimer's Association- 1-800-272-3900
- American Cancer Society- 1-866-228-4327
- American Diabetes Association- 1-800-342-2383
- American Heart and Stroke Association- 1-800-242-8721
- American Parkinson's Disease Association- 1-800-223-2732

Citations

1. *Caregiving in the U.S.* (2004, April). Retrieved May 2008, from National Alliance for Caregiving and AARP: http://www.caregiving.org/data/04finalreport.pdf

2. Biegel, D. E., & Wieder, B. L. (n.d.). *Caregiving - Formal, Informal, Definition of Family Caregiving*. Retrieved May 2008, from JRank: http://family.jrank.org/pages/202/Caregiving.html

3. *Selected Caregiver Statistics*. (n.d.). Retrieved May 2008, from Family Caregiver Alliance: http://www.caregiver.org/caregiver/jsp/content_node.jsp?nodeid=439

4. *Depression and Alzheimer's*. (2008, April 14). Retrieved May 2008, from Medical News Today: http://www.medicalnewstoday.com/articles/103908.php

5. *Caregiver: When Stress Turns Into Depression: Getting Help, Having Hope*. (2005, November 1). Retrieved May 2008, from WebMD: http://www.webmd.com/balance/stress-management/stress-turns-to-depression

6. Brain, M. (n.d.). *How Laughter Works*. Retrieved May 2008, from HowStuffWorks: http://people.howstuffworks.com/laughter.htm

7. Ibid

8. *Optimists Live Longer* . (2000, February 8). Retrieved May 2008, from BBC News: http://news.bbc.co.uk/2/hi/health/635292.stm

9. Anderson, S. (2007, February 12). *Making Sense of Astronaut Lisa Marie's Actions*. Retrieved May 2008, from Third Age: http://blog.thirdage.com/?p=908

10. Dharma Singh Khalsa, M. (n.d.). *Four Pillars of Building a Better Memory, Pillar 2: Stress Management*. Retrieved May 2008, from Alzheimer's Research and Prevention Foundation: http://www.alzheimersprevention.org/pillar_2.htm

11. Richard O'Connor, P. (n.d.). *Stress Kill Brain Cells*. Retrieved May 2008, from Google: http://groups.google.com/group/alt.support/browse_thread/thread/41483b6f54cb930d

12. *Non-pharmacologic management of agitated behaviors in persons with Alzheimer disease and other chronic dementing illnesses*. (n.d.). Retrieved May 2008, from National Guideline Clearhinghouse: http://www.guideline.gov/summary/summary.aspx?ss=15&doc_id=6221&nbr=3992

13. *Tips for Improving Communication Skills for Caregivers*. (n.d.). Retrieved May 2008, from WorkingCaregiver: http://www.workingcaregiver.com/articles/caregiving/improvingcommunications

14. *Caregiver's Guide to Understanding Dementia Behaviors* . (n.d.).
    Retrieved May 2008, from Family Caregiver Alliance:
    http://www.caregiver.org/caregiver/jsp/content_node.jsp?nodeid=391

15. Dr. Bob Judd, D. a. (2003, November 4). *Texas Vet News Healthy People
    and Pets*. Retrieved May 2008, from Veterinary Partner:
    http://www.veterinarypartner.com/Content.plx?P=A&C=32&A=1875&S=0

16. *Paws That Refresh: A Dose of Puppy Love - Pet Visits Help Patients
    Heal*. (n.d.). Retrieved May 2008, from Northridge Hospital:
    http://www.northridgehospital.org/stellent/groups/public/@xinternet_con
    _nnc/documents/webcontent/180299.pdf

17. *Non-pharmacologic management of agitated behaviors in persons with
    Alzheimer disease and other chronic dementing illnesses,* op. cit.

18. Rick Nauert, P. (2007, September 18). *Caregiver Stress Can Shorten
    Life*. Retrieved May 2008, from PsychCentral:
    http://psychcentral.com/news/2007/09/18/caregiver-stress-can-shorten-
    life/1290.html

19. Kornblum, J. (2005, July 13). *Love Guides in Alzheimer's Care* .
    Retrieved May 2008, from USA TODAY :
    http://www.usatoday.com/news/health/2005-07-13-alzheimers-
    caregivers_x.htm

20. *The Effects of Stress on Your Body*. (2006, December). Retrieved May
    2008, from WebMD: http://www.webmd.com/content/pages/7/1674_52147.htm

21. Ibid

22. Davis, J. L. (2008, March 21). *Coping With Anxiety, Tip: Change What
    You Can, Accept the Rest*. Retrieved May 2008, from WebMD:
    http://www.webmd.com/anxiety-panic/guide/coping-with-anxiety

23. *Stress Kill Brain Cells,* op. cit.

24. *Coping With Anxiety, Tip: Change What You Can, Accept the Rest,* op.
    cit.

25. Terzella, M. E. (2007). *Break Free From Worry, Can't pack up your cares
    and woes? Here's what you can do!* Retrieved May 2008, from Caring
    Today: http://www.caringtoday.com/just-for-you/break-free-from-worry

26. Buckley, C. (2007, January 3). *Man Is Rescued by Stranger on Subway
    Tracks*. Retrieved May 2008, from New York Times:
    http://www.nytimes.com/2007/01/03/nyregion/03life.html?_r=1&ref=nyregio
    n&oref=slogin

27. *The Effects of Stress on Your Body*, op. cit.

28. *Renew-Stress on the Brain*. (n.d.). Retrieved May 2008, from Franklin
    Institute : http://www.fi.edu/learn/brain/stress.html

29. *Stress & Your Health: Tips for Reducing Stress*. (2006, December).
    Retrieved May 2008, from WebMD:
    http://www.webmd.com/solutions/sc/stressed_out/stress-tips

30. *Relaxation and Other Alternative Approaches for Managing Headaches*.
    (2007, August 25). Retrieved May 2008, from Cleveland Clinic:
    http://www.clevelandclinic.org/health/health-
    info/docs/3400/3470.asp?index=11664

31. *Stress Kill Brain Cells*, op. cit.

32. Reiss, V. (2008, January/February). *Sharpen Your Brain, Hey, Einstein!*
    Yeah, we're taking to you. Never mind how many brain cells you've fried
    on the weekends--this genius guide to your gray matter will have your
    neurons firing like AK-47s. Retrieved May 2008, from Women's Health
    Magazine: http://www.womenshealthmag.com/health/sharpen-your-
    brain?page=2

33. Chase, A. (n.d.). *How to use an Affirmation*. Retrieved May 2008, from
    ehow: http://www.ehow.com/how_2101073_use-an-affirmation.html

34. *What is Aromatherapy?* (n.d.). Retrieved May 2008, from HolisticOnline:
    http://www.holisticonline.com/Aromatherapy/aroma_what_is.htm

35. Robert W. Griffith, M. (2004, December 16). *Alzheimer's, Aromatherapy,*
    and Bright Lights. Retrieved May 2008, from Health and Age:
    http://www.healthandage.com/public/health-
    center/11/article/2151/Alzheimers-Aromatherapy-and-Bright-Lights.html

36. *Alzheimer's Disease and Dementia* . (n.d.). Retrieved May 2008, from
    Birch Hill Happenings: http://birchhillhappenings.com/dementia.htm

37. *Music Therapy*. (n.d.). Retrieved May 2008, from HolisticOnline:
    http://holisticonline.com/Stress/stress_music-therapy.htm

38. Ibid

39. Ibid

40. Ibid

41. *Relaxation and Other Alternative Approaches for Managing Headaches*, op.
    cit.

42. Lytle, R. (2008). *Music Therapy, The Healing Power of Music*. Retrieved
    May 2008, from Wings Cancer Foundation:
    http://www.wingscancerfoundation.org/index.cfm?section=3&page=39

43. *Music Therapy*, op. cit.

44. Ibid

45. Lindberg, K. A. (1998, June 20). *What is Music Therapy?* Retrieved May
    2008, from Music Therapy Info Link:
    http://members.aol.com/kathysl/def.html

46. *Medical Encyclopedia: Music Therapy.* (2008). Retrieved May 2008, from Answers.com: http://www.answers.com/topic/music-therapy?cat=entertainment

47. *Music Therapy and Mental Health.* (n.d.). Retrieved May 2008, from American Music Therapy Association, Inc.: http://www.musictherapy.org/factsheets/MT%20Mental%20Health%202006.pdf

48. *What is Music Therapy?* , op. cit.

49. Palmer, C. (n.d.). *The Profound Effects of Music on the Mind.* Retrieved May 2008, from Synapse: The UCSF Student Newspaper: http://www.ucsf.edu/synapse/articles/2008/Apr/17/musictherapy.html

50. *What is music therapy? Answers* . (2007, November 15). Retrieved May 2008, from Ibibo: http://sawaal.ibibo.com/ViewAnswers.aspx?quesId=f930489d-05b2-4226-95e0-c8e4395d2a1e&sb=k&catcityid=36&tab=L&shorturl=what-music-therapy-204622&csurl=music

51. *Play a Song, or Sing Along, for Alzheimer's* . (2006, February 1). Retrieved May 2008, from Fisher Center for Alzheimer's Research Foundation: http://www.alzinfo.org/newsarticle/templates/archivenewstemplate.asp?articleid=191&zoneid=8

52. O'Donnell, L. (1999). *Music and the Brain* . Retrieved May 2008, from http://www.cerebromente.org.br/n15/mente/musica.html

53. Baumel, S. (1995). *Dealing with Depression Naturally.* New Canaan, Conn.: Keats Publishing.

54. *Music Therapy*, op. cit.

55. Cottrel, A. (2000). *What is Healing Music? Healing Music—A Closer Look.* Retrieved May 2008, from Vox Mundi Project: http://www.voxmundiproject.com/recommended_readings_6.htm

56. *What is Music Therapy?* , op. cit.

57. Ibid

58. *What is Healing Music? Healing Music—A Closer Look*, op. cit.

59. *Music Therapy, The Healing Power of Music*, op. cit.

60. Ibid

61. *Research Conducted On Music Therapy for Depression.* (n.d.). Retrieved May 2008, from AlternateHeals.com: http://www.alternateheals.com/music-therapy/music-therapy-depression.htm

62. *Listening to Music Can Reduce Chronic Pain and Depression By Up to A Quarter.* (2006, May 24). Retrieved May 2008, from The Journal of Advanced Nursing:

http://www.journalofadvancednursing.com/default.asp?File=pressdetail&id=173

63. *What is Healing Music? Healing Music—A Closer Look*, op. cit.

64. *Dealing with Depression Naturally*, op. cit.

65. Peters, D. (n.d.). *How To Deal With Depression Naturally*. Retrieved May 2008, from ehow: http://www.ehow.com/how_2117072_deal-depression-naturally.html

66. *What is Healing Music? Healing Music—A Closer Look*, op. cit.

67. *Dealing with Depression Naturally*, op. cit.

68. *Music Therapy*, op. cit.

69. *Play a Song, or Sing Along, for Alzheimer's*, op. cit.

70. *Music Therapy*, op. cit.

71. *What is Healing Music? Healing Music—A Closer Look*, op. cit.

72. *Music Therapy*, op. cit.

73. Ibid

74. *Alzheimer's Disease*. (2007). Retrieved May 2008, from Encyclopedia of Mental Disorders: http://www.minddisorders.com/A-Br/Alzheimer-s-disease.html

75. *Play a Song, or Sing Along, for Alzheimer's*, op. cit.

76. *Music Therapy*, op. cit.

77. Ibid

78. Ibid

79. *Music and the Brain*, op. cit.

80. Brewer, C. (2002). *Focus and Concentration*. Retrieved May 2008, from Songs For Teaching: http://www.songsforteaching.com/brewer/welcoming.htm

81. Daisy T. Lu, P. (n.d.). *Music Education Beyond the Mozart Effect*. Retrieved May 2008, from Neuroscience for Kids: http://faculty.washington.edu/chudler/dl.html

82. *Music and the Brain*, op. cit.

83. *Play a Song, or Sing Along, for Alzheimer's*, op. cit.

84. Ibid

85. Ibid

86. Ibid

87. Ibid

88. Ibid

89. Harkins, D. (2007). *Healing With Music: How song soothes those in need of care*. Retrieved May 2008, from Caring Today: http://www.caringtoday.com/put-ideas-into-practice/healing-with-music

90. Ibid

91. Ibid

92. *Play a Song, or Sing Along, for Alzheimer's*, op. cit.

93. *Depression Music Therapy to Overcome Self Isolation*. (2008). Retrieved May 2008, from AlternateHeals.com: http://www.alternateheals.com/music-therapy/depression-music-therapy.htm

94. Ibid

95. Beardsley, N. (2006, March 14). *First World Parkinson's Congress Spotlights Therapeutic Effects of Music*. Retrieved May 2008, from Voice of America: http://www.voanews.com/english/archive/2006-03/2006-03-14-voa65.cfm?CFID=302262826&CFTOKEN=14913023

96. Cromley, J. (2008, March 3). *Music found to help stroke victims* . Retrieved May 2008, from Los Angeles Times: http://www.knoxnews.com/news/2008/Mar/03/music-found-to-help-stroke-victims/

97. Michele Brunges, G. A. (2003, November). *Music therapy for reducing surgical anxiety - Clinical Innovations*. Retrieved May 2008, from AORN Journal, BNet: http://findarticles.com/p/articles/mi_m0FSL/is_5_78/ai_111011829

98. *Soundmasker*. (2007). Retrieved May 2008, from Vector Media Software: http://www.vectormediasoftware.com/soundmaskerinfo.htm

99. David A. Smith, M. C. (2003, April 28). *Behavioral and Environmental Interventions*. Retrieved May 2008, from Quality Matters: http://qmweb.dads.state.tx.us/BehaviorMgm.htm

100. *Music Therapy*, op. cit.

101. Mary Calvagna, M. (2006, January). *Tips For Getting A Good Night Sleep*. Retrieved May 2008, from Health Library: https://healthlibrary.epnet.com/GetContent.aspx?token=af362d97-4f80-4453-a175-02cc6220a387&chunkiid=10066

102. Kase, L. M. (2007, October). *The Magic Power of Sleep: How it Makes You Happier, Healthier, Sexier, Even Thinner*. Retrieved May 2008, from Reader's Digest: http://www.rd.com/living-healthy/the-magic-power-of-sleep/article45808.html

103. Ibid

104. *Memory and Morpheus* . (2007, October 12). Retrieved May 2008, from
Revolution Health, Content provided by Posit Science
(www.positscience.com) :
http://www.revolutionhealth.com/conditions/brain-nerves/brain-
health/memory/memory-morpheus

105. Ibid

106. Ibid

107. Ibid

108. Lennon, S. T. (2007, September 23). *Long-term insomnia puts you at
risk*. Retrieved May 2008, from USA Weekend:
http://www.usaweekend.com/07_issues/070923/070923health-briefs.html

109. *The Magic Power of Sleep: How it Makes You Happier, Healthier, Sexier,
Even Thinner*, op. cit.

110. *Tips For Getting A Good Night Sleep*, op. cit.

111. *Lack of Sleep Linked to Increased Risk of High Blood Pressure*. (2006,
April 3). Retrieved May 2008, from Columbia University Medical Center:
http://www.cumc.columbia.edu/news/press_releases/gangwisch_sleep_blood_
pressure.html

112. *The Magic Power of Sleep: How it Makes You Happier, Healthier, Sexier,
Even Thinner*, op. cit.

113. *The Importance of Sleep and Health*. (n.d.). Retrieved May 2008, from
Harvard Health Publications:
http://www.health.harvard.edu/press_releases/importance_of_sleep_and_he
alth.htm

114. *Tips For Getting A Good Night Sleep*, op. cit.

115. *The Magic Power of Sleep: How it Makes You Happier, Healthier, Sexier,
Even Thinner*, op. cit.

116. *Tips For Getting A Good Night Sleep*, op. cit.

117. *The Magic Power of Sleep: How it Makes You Happier, Healthier, Sexier,
Even Thinner*, op. cit.

118. *The Importance of Sleep and Health*, op. cit

119. *The Magic Power of Sleep: How it Makes You Happier, Healthier, Sexier,
Even Thinner*, op. cit.

120. Eve Van Cauter, P. (2007, October). *Something to Lose Sleep Over –
Sleep Loss and Your Health*. Retrieved May 2008, from The Doctor Will
See You Now:
http://www.thedoctorwillseeyounow.com/articles/behavior/sleep_16/#back1
4

121. *Tips For Getting A Good Night Sleep*, op. cit.

122. *Are some people more likely to get vascular dementia?* (2007, August). Retrieved May 2008, from Alzheimer's Society: http://www.alzheimers.org.uk/factsheet/402

123. *Tired of feeling tired? Experts provide sleep solutions.* (2008, February 29). Retrieved May 2008, from Moorpark Acorn, North American Precis Syndicate Inc.: http://www.moorparkacorn.com/news/2008/0229/health_and_wellness/042.html

124. Ibid

125. Roberts, S. (2007, March/April). *At Last! A Good Night's Sleep.* Retrieved May 2008, from AARP Magazine: http://www.aarpmagazine.org/health/good_nights_sleep.html

126. *Tired of feeling tired? Experts provide sleep solutions*, op. cit.

127. *Tips For Getting A Good Night Sleep*, op. cit.

128. Ibid

129. *Stress Kill Brain Cells,* op. cit.

130. *Sleep Disorders Health Center: Behavioral Treatments* . (2007, August 1). Retrieved May 2008, from WebMD: http://www.webmd.com/sleep-disorders/behavioral-treatments

131. *Bright Light Therapy: What is it?* (2006, May 11). Retrieved May 2008, from American Academy of Sleep Medicine, Sleep Education.com: http://www.sleepeducation.com/Treatment.aspx?id=4

132. *At Last! A Good Night's Sleep*, op. cit.

133. *Memory and Morpheus*, op. cit.

134. *Tips For Getting A Good Night Sleep*, op. cit

135. *Tired of feeling tired? Experts provide sleep solutions*, op. cit.

136. Youdin, J. (2007, March/April). *Try This First: Sleep Hygiene.* Retrieved May 2008, from AARP Magazine: http://www.aarpmagazine.org/health/sleep_hygiene.html

137. *Tired of feeling tired? Experts provide sleep solutions*, op. cit.

138. *Tips For Getting A Good Night Sleep*, op. cit.

139. Ibid

140. *Try This First: Sleep Hygiene*, op. cit.

141. Ibid

142. Ibid

143. *Tips For Getting A Good Night Sleep*, op. cit.

144. Ibid

145. Ibid

146. *Memory and Morpheus*, op. cit.

147. *Tips For Getting A Good Night Sleep*, op. cit.

148. *Try This First: Sleep Hygiene*, op. cit.

149. *Tired of feeling tired? Experts provide sleep solutions*, op. cit.

150. *Tips For Getting A Good Night Sleep*, op. cit.

151. Derbyshire, D. (2008, February 21). *How A Six-Minute Power Nap Can Improve Your Memory*. Retrieved May 2008, from Daily Mail: http://www.dailymail.co.uk/health/article-517118/How-minute-power-nap-improve-memory.html

152. Ibid

153. Ibid

154. Ibid

155. *Love Guides in Alzheimer's Care*, op. cit.

156. *The Magic Power of Sleep: How it Makes You Happier, Healthier, Sexier, Even Thinner*, op. cit.

157. *Sundowning*. (n.d.). Retrieved May 2008, from The Alzheimer's Association of Los Angeles: http://www.alzla.org/dementia/sundowning.html

158. Ibid

159. Fallon, J. (2006, June 29). *Learning Counteracts Stress*. Retrieved May 2008, from Third Age: http://blog.thirdage.com/?p=628

160. Patoine, B. (2007, May 1). *Move Your Feet, Grow New Neurons? Exercise-Induced Neurogenesis Shown in Humans*. Retrieved May 2008, from The Dana Foundation: http://www.dana.org/news/brainwork/detail.aspx?id=7374

161. *Study: Staying active helps keep the mind sharp, Older people who exercise regularly are less likely to develop dementia*. (2006, January 16). Retrieved May 2008, from MSNBC: http://www.msnbc.msn.com/id/10877612/

162. *Gene May Keep the Mind Sharp into Old Age*. (2007, January 2). Retrieved May 2008, from Fisher Center for Alzheimer's Research Foundation:

http://www.alzinfo.org/newsarticle/templates/newstemplate.asp?articleid
=205&zoneid=4

163. *Obesity Linked to Increased Risk for Dementia.* (2008, May 13).
Retrieved May 2008, from Sun Sentinel: http://www.sun-
sentinel.com/features/health/sfl-
fljjpsdementia0513jjdcmay13,0,1352474.story

164. *Obesity in Middle Age Increases Risk of Dementia Later in Life.* (2005,
April 27). Retrieved May 2008, from Kaiser Permanente Northern
California News Bureau :
http://www.dor.kaiser.org/dors/news/April2005_ObesityDementia_Whitmer.s
html

165. Gever, J. (2008, March 13). *AHA Nutrition: A Little Exercise Goes A
Long Way for Overweight Older Women* . Retrieved May 2008, from MedPage
Today : http://www.medpagetoday.com/PrimaryCare/ExerciseFitness/tb/8717

166. Shelton Duruisseau, P. (2007, July 18). *Physician Wellness as
Constrained by Burnout* . Retrieved May 2008, from State of California
Department of Consumer Affairs, Medical Board of California :
http://www.mbc.ca.gov/licensee/physician_wellness.pdf

167. Michael W. Smith, M. (2005, June 29). *Tips for Reducing Stress.*
Retrieved May 2008, from WebMD:
http://www.webmd.com/content/Article/62/71546.htm

168. Haughton, N. (2007). *Advice You Can Take To Heart Mediterranean-
Inspired Diet From Cleveland Clinic Is Good ...And Good For You.*
Retrieved May 2008, from Daily News, The Free Library:
http://www.thefreelibrary.com/ADVICE+YOU+CAN+TAKE+TO+HEART+MEDITERRANEA
N-INSPIRED+DIET+FROM+...-a0159974406

169. *Sundowning and Sleep Disturbances.* (2007, Fall). Retrieved May 2008,
from Alzhiemer's Association:
http://64.26.26.159/pdfs/newsletterfiles/NORVAL/fall07nvly.pdf

170. *Insomnia.* (n.d.). Retrieved May 2008, from Health24:
http://www.health24.com/mind/Psychology_A_Z/1284-1307,12339.asp

171. *Physical Activity Benefits Nursing-Home Residents with Alzheimer's.*
(2007 , Apri 17). Retrieved May 2008, from Fisher Center for
Alzheimer's Research Foundation:
http://www.alzinfo.org/newsarticle/templates/newstemplate.asp?articleid
=219&zoneid=1

172. *Exercise: A Guide From the National Institute on Aging.* (2004, April).
Retrieved May 2008, from National Institute on Aging:
http://www.niapublications.org/exercisebook/ExerciseGuideComplete.pdf

173. Ibid

174. Laurie LaRusso, M. E. (2006, January). *Start a Regular Exercise
Program.* Retrieved May 2008, from Third Age:
http://www.thirdage.com/healthgate/files/21333.html

175. *Exercise: A Guide From the National Institute on Aging*, op. cit.

176. *A healthier, fitter YOU — Simple strength training tips* . (2007, May 10). Retrieved May 2008, from Harvard Health Publications: http://www.health.harvard.edu/healthbeat/HEALTHbeat_051007.htm

177. Ibid

178. *Start a Regular Exercise Program*, op. cit.

179. *Exercise: A Guide From the National Institute on Aging*, op. cit.

180. *Tai chi: Improved stress reduction, balance, agility for all*. (2007, November 15). Retrieved May 2008, from Mayo Clinic: http://www.mayoclinic.com/health/tai-chi/SA00087

181. Ecclesiastes (ch. I, v. 14)

182. Rebecca A. Seguin, B. C. (2002). *Growing Stronger – Strength Training for Older Adults*. Retrieved May 2008, from Center for Disease Control and Prevention: http://www.cdc.gov/nccdphp/dnpa/physical/growing_stronger/growing_stron ger.pdf

183. Ibid

184. Ibid

185. Ibid

186. Ibid

187. *Falls Among Older Adults: An Overview*. (n.d.). Retrieved May 2008, from Center for Disease Control and Prevention : http://www.cdc.gov/ncipc/factsheets/adultfalls.htm

188. *Drug Maker: Bone Drug Cuts Elderly Deaths, Breaks*. (2007, September 18). Retrieved May 2008, from Fox News: http://www.foxnews.com/story/0,2933,297150,00.html?sPage=fnc/health/lon gevity

189. Gandel, C. (2007). *Fear of Falling, Ways to Help the Person in Your Care Conquer This Very Real Concern*. Retrieved May 2008, from Caring Today: http://www.caringtoday.com/put-ideas-into-practice/fear-of-falling

190. *Your Guide to Fall Prevention: How to Prevent One of the Most Catastrophic Events in the Life of a Senior*. (n.d.). Retrieved May 2008, from Compassionate Senior Care, Senior's Choice : http://www.compassionateseniorcare.com/PDFs/FallPreventionBrochure.pdf

191. *Fear of Falling, Ways to Help the Person in Your Care Conquer This Very Real Concern*, op. cit.

192. Gever, J. (2008, March 7). *Even Minor Injuries from Falls May Inspire Long-Lasting Fears In Seniors* . Retrieved May 2008, from MedPage Today: http://www.medpagetoday.com/Geriatrics/GeneralGeriatrics/tb/8641

193. *Fall Prevention: 6 ways to Reduce Your Falling Risk.* (2008 , January 11). Retrieved May 2008, from Mayo Clinic: http://www.mayoclinic.com/health/fall-prevention/HQ00657

194. Erik Peper, P. (2007, September 1). *Better Balance, Fewer Falls.* Retrieved May 2008, from Bottom Line Secrets: http://www.bottomlinesecrets.com/blpnet/article.html?article_id=42922

195. *Growing Stronger - Strength Training for Older Adults,* op. cit.

196. *Better Balance Prevents Falls.* (n.d.). Retrieved May 2008, from AARP: http://www.aarp.org/health/staying_healthy/prevention/better_balance_pr events_falls.html

197. *Better Balance, Fewer Falls,* op. cit.

198. Ibid

199. Ibid

200. *Mediterranean Diet.* (n.d.). Retrieved May 2008, from American Heart Association: http://www.americanheart.org/presenter.jhtml?identifier=4644

201. Ibid

202. *Advice You Can Take To Heart Mediterranean-Inspired Diet From Cleveland Clinic Is Good ...And Good For You,* op. cit.

203. Nikolaos Scarmeas, M., Yaakov Stern, P., Richard Mayeux, M., & Jose A. Luchsinger, M. (2006, December). *Mediterranean Diet, Alzheimer Disease, and Vascular Mediation.* Retrieved May 2008, from Archives of Neurology: http://archneur.ama-assn.org/cgi/content/full/63/12/1709

204. *2008 Alzheimer's Disease Facts and Figures.* (2008). Retrieved May 2008, from Alzheimer's Association: http://www.alz.org/national/documents/report_alzfactsfigures2008.pdf

205. *Food For Thought.* (n.d.). Retrieved May 2008, from Third Age: http://www.thirdage.com/news/articles/ALT02/08/02/22/ALT02080222-01.html

206. Ibid

207. Ibid

208. Ibid

209. Groch, J. (2007, September 10). *Mediterranean Diet May Prolong Life of Alzheimer's Patients.* Retrieved May 2008, from MedPage Today: http://www.medpagetoday.com/Geriatrics/Dementia/tb/6641

210. Holder, D. (2006, October 15). *Watch What You Eat, and Go Easy on the Caffeine: Aim for Balanced Meals and Try to Avoid Large Portions of Unhealthy Fare That Can Stress Your System.* Retrieved May 2008, from Red Orbit, The Miami Herald: http://www.redorbit.com/news/business/693225/watch_what_you_eat_and_go_easy_on_the_caffeine/index.html

211. Karen Ansel, M. R. (n.d.). *The DNA of Antioxidants.* Retrieved May 2008, from Cooking Light: http://www.cookinglight.com/cooking/hl/nutrition/package/0,14343,1738449,00.html

212. Ibid

213. Ibid

214. Ibid

215. Ibid

216. Haughton, N. (2007, February 2). *Tips for a heart-healthy living.* Retrieved May 2008, from Daily News: http://www.dailynews.com/ci_5212718

217. Mitchell, S. (2007, September 5). *Breakfast the New Brain Food.* Retrieved May 2008, from Third Age: http://blog.thirdage.com/?p=1114

218. WenYen Juan, P. P. (2004, Winter). *More than one in three older Americans may not drink enough water: insight 27 September 2002.* Retrieved May 2008, from BNet: http://findarticles.com/p/articles/mi_m0EUB/is_1_16/ai_n6206909

219. Sandy Killam-Hall, M. R. (n.d.). *Hydration—A Great Sensation.* Retrieved May 2008, from Fordham University: www.fordham.edu/images/facilities/food/pds/wellness.pdf

220. *Water: How much should you drink every day?* (2008, April 19). Retrieved May 2008, from Mayo Clinic: http://www.mayoclinic.com/health/water/NU00283

221. *Water Facts.* (n.d.). Retrieved May 2008, from Freshwater Society: http://www.freshwater.org/water-facts.html

222. Dr. David S. Dyer, N. (n.d.). *Water, the Essence of Life.* Retrieved May 2008, from Valley Water: www.valleywater.net

223. Ibid

224. *Hydration—A Great Sensation*, op. cit.

225. Karen Hambly, B. (n.d.). *Hydration.* Retrieved May 2008, from Valley Water: www.valleywater.net

226. Ibid

227. Ibid

228. Kimberly Beauchamp, N. (2008, February 14). *New Food Pyramid Supports Seniors'*. Retrieved May 2008, from Health Monthly: http://www.healthmonthly.co.uk/health/news/newswire_2008_02_14_1.html

229. *Brain Malfunction Explains Dehydration In Elderly*. (2007, December 18). Retrieved May 2008, from Science Daily: http://www.sciencedaily.com/releases/2007/12/071217192400.htm

230. *Hydration*, op. cit.

231. *Hydration—A Great Sensation*, op. cit.

232. *Hydration*, op. cit.

233. *Hydration—A Great Sensation*, op. cit.

234. Ibid

235. *Dehydration: How to Recognize and Prevent Its Effects*. (2008, March 21). Retrieved May 2008, from Medicine Net: http://www.medicinenet.com/dehydration/article.htm

236. *Dehydration*. (2007, January 3). Retrieved May 2008, from Mayo Clinic: http://www.mayoclinic.com/health/dehydration/DS00561/DSECTION=2

237. *Dehydration: How to Recognize and Prevent Its Effects*, op. cit.

238. *Water, the Essence of Life*, op. cit.

239. Ibid

240. Marilyn S. Albert, P. (2007, August 2). *Changing the Trajectory of Cognitive Decline*. Retrieved May 2008, from New England Journal of Medicine: http://content.nejm.org/cgi/content/extract/357/5/502

241. *2008 Alzheimer's Disease Facts and Figures*, op. cit.

242. *Mentally Stimulating Leisure Activities May Ward Off Alzheimer's*. (2008, January 15). Retrieved May 2008, from Fisher Center for Alzheimer's Research Foundation: http://www.alzinfo.org/newsarticle/templates/newstemplate.asp?articleid=259&zoneid=4

243. Ibid

244. Dr. David Snowdon, P. (2003, September 23). *The Nun Study FAQ's,*. Retrieved May 2008, from Nun Study: http://www.mc.uky.edu/nunnet/

245. Robert S. Wilson, P., Carlos F. Mendes de Leon, P., Lisa L. Barnes, P., Julie A. Schneider, M., Julia L. Bienias, S., Denis A. Evans, M., et al. (2002, February 13). *Participation in Cognitively Stimulating Activities and Risk of Incident Alzheimer Disease*. Retrieved May 2008, from The Journal of American Medical Association: http://jama.ama-assn.org/cgi/content/abstract/287/6/742?maxtoshow=&HITS=10&hits=10&RESULTFORMAT=&fulltext=participation+in+cognitively+stimulating+activities+

and+the+risk+of+alzheimers%27s+disease&searchid=1122502876647_490&store
d_search=&FIRSTINDEX=0&jou

246. *Mentally Stimulating Leisure Activities May Ward Off Alzheimer's*, op. cit.

247. *Loneliness Associated with Increased Risk of Alzheimer's Disease.* (2007, February 5). Retrieved May 2008, from Rush University Medical Center : http://www.rush.edu/webapps/MEDREL/servlet/NewsRelease?ID=844

248. *Non-pharmacologic management of agitated behaviors in persons with Alzheimer disease and other chronic dementing illnesses,* op. cit.

249. *Brain Exercises Sharpen Memory in Older Adults.* (2007, November 19). Retrieved May 2008, from Bio-Medicine: http://www.bio-medicine.org/medicine-news-1/Brain-Exercises-Sharpen-Memory-in-Older-Adults-6567-1/

250. Sherry L. Willis, P., Sharon L. Tennstedt, P., Michael Marsiske, P., Karlene Ball, P., Jeffrey Elias, P., Kathy Mann Koepke, P., et al. (2006, December 20). *Study on the Long Term Effects of Cognitive Training on Everyday Functional Outcomes in Older Adults.* Retrieved May 2008, from The Journal of the American Medical Association: http://jama.ama-assn.org/cgi/content/abstract/296/23/2805

251. *Changing the Trajectory of Cognitive Decline*, op. cit.

252. *Learning Counteracts Stress*, op. cit.

253. *Brain Plasticity: What is It?* (n.d.). Retrieved May 2008, from Neuroscience for Kids: http://faculty.washington.edu/chudler/plast.html

254. *How Big Is Your Brain? Its Size May Protect You from Memory Loss.* (2008, April 15). Retrieved May 2008, from Academy of Neurology: http://www.aan.com/press/index.cfm?fuseaction=release.view&release=591

255. *Five Steps to Fight Dementia.* (n.d.). Retrieved May 2008, from Third Age: http://www.thirdage.com/news/articles/ALT02/05/12/16/ALT02051216-01.html

256. *Brain Plasticity: What is It?*, op. cit.

257. *How Chocolate, Cold Cuts and Sex Boost Your Brain.* (n.d.). Retrieved May 2008, from Third Age : http://www.thirdage.com/news/articles/DAI/07/12/20/071220-01.html

258. Ibid

259. Samples, P. (2007, March 26). *Creativity Gets Better with Age.* Retrieved May 2008, from Third Age: http://blog.thirdage.com/?p=950

260. Schmid, R. E. (2008, March 21). *Science, Bible Agree: Giving is Better* . Retrieved May 2008, from Christian Post: http://www.christianpost.com/article/20080321/31610_Science,_Bible_Agree:_Giving_is_Better_.htm

261. *Kindness and Health.* (1999, June). Retrieved May 2008, from Kindness.com: http://www.kindness.com.au/kindness_and_health.htm

262. Ibid

263. Ibid

264. Ibid

265. *Kindness: How Good Deeds Can Be Good For You!* (n.d.). Retrieved May 2008, from Random Acts of Kindness Foundation : http://www.actsofkindness.org/inspiration/health/detail.asp?id=1

266. Ibid

267. Ibid